D1261201

Cooperative
Rural Electrification

James E. Ross

James Elmer Ross II

Published in cooperation with
National Rural Electric
Cooperative Association

The Praeger Special Studies program—
utilizing the most modern and efficient book
production techniques and a selective
worldwide distribution network—makes
available to the academic, government, and
business communities significant, timely
research in U.S. and international economic, social, and political development.

Cooperative
Rural Electrification
Case Studies of Pilot
Projects in Latin America

HD9688
.L32 R68

PRAEGER SPECIAL STUDIES IN INTERNATIONAL ECONOMICS AND DEVELOPMENT

Praeger Publishers   New York   Washington   London

INDIANA PURDUE LIBRARY DEC 1973 FORT WAYNE

WITHDRAWN

PRAEGER PUBLISHERS
111 Fourth Avenue, New York, N.Y. 10003, U.S.A.
5, Cromwell Place, London S.W.7, England

Published in the United States of America in 1972

All rights reserved

Library of Congress Catalog Card Number: 77-149281

Printed in the United States of America

This is a book about rural electric cooperatives in less developed countries--the first electrification of rural areas to be financed through the U.S. foreign aid program. The study attempts to determine initial impact of cooperative electrification on development of rural areas in four countries (Colombia, Costa Rica, Ecuador and Nicaragua) and, hence, implications for international development.

One of the primary objectives is to provide an understanding of the existing situation before the impact of rural electrification. Background material is provided for establishing base lines from which changes in the rural social and economic systems can be viewed in years to come. The study focuses primarily on the economies of the areas, although some data are presented on the ecological, demographic, governmental and educational systems.

Almost all data are gathered from primary sources. Unfortunately, there is little secondary data available on rural areas in developing countries. It is also unfortunate that there has been little research anywhere in the world on the economic and social effects of rural electrification. Programs, generally, were undertaken because of political or social pressure, or, in some cases, to bolster wartime production. Time was not taken to analyze the effects of rural electrification on economic and social development.

This is of prime consideration in allocation of international and domestic funds to achieve development in low-income countries. If developing countries are to justify investments in rural electrification on the basis of economic development, utilization of energy must be in such a manner that it increases the productivity of rural inhabitants. If investments are to be justified on the basis of social progress, electricity and the mechanism for its distribution must improve individual and community welfare.

ACKNOWLEDGMENTS

The field study, on which much of this book is based, would have been impossible to conduct without the cooperation and assistance of many people. Especially helpful were the rural families in Latin America who so willingly provided information on their farm operations. Talking with these people and visiting their homes and communities was an inspiration.

Special acknowledgment is due Manuel Criales, Carlos Gil, Stan Allen, Manuel Guerrero, Diego Pardo, Wilfred Mast, John Taylor and David Leon for assisting with interviews and reporting on observations in the various countries.

A study by Galen Moses in Costa Rica was drawn on heavily for information included in Chapter 3. The author benefited from consultations on Chapter 2 with Professors Thomas Hieronymus, Folke Dovring and Earl Swanson of the University of Illinois. Dr. Thomas Venables and Leon Evans of the National Rural Electric Cooperative Association reviewed drafts of this book and offered valuable suggestions. To all of them I extend my sincere appreciation.

At all stages in the preparation of this book I benefited from the encouragement of my wife, Barbara B. Ross. For this I am grateful.

CONTENTS

LIST OF TABLES

xxiii

LIST OF MAPS

LIST OF ABBREVIATIONS

AID	U.S. Agency for International Development
CVC	Corporacion Autonoma Regional de Cauca
GNP	Gross National Product
HP	Horsepower
INECEL	Instituto Ecuatoriano de Electrificacion
KRECC	Kentucky Rural Electric Cooperative Corporation
KV	Kilovolt
KVA	Kilovolt-amperes
KW	Kilowatt
KWH	Kilowatt-hour
NESC	U.S. National Electric Safety Code
NRECA	National Rural Electric Cooperative Association
REA	Rural Electrification Administration
SENA	Servicio Nacional de Aprendizaje

GLOSSARY

<u>Cacao</u>	Cocoa.
<u>Corregimiento</u>	Similar to a U.S. township; smaller than a municipio.
<u>Department</u>	Similar to a U.S. state.
<u>Municipio</u>	Similar to a U.S. county.
<u>Panela</u>	Unrefined brown sugar.
<u>Platano</u>	A banana plant. Starchy fruit that is a staple food throughout the tropics when cooked. (1 racimo equals 1 stalk.)
<u>Racimo</u>	Stalk.
<u>Rural Electric Cooperative</u>	A non-profit organization of people in rural towns, villages and farms who have joined together to form a legally incorporated cooperative for the purpose of supplying its members with electric service at the least cost.
<u>Rural Electrification</u>	Rural electrification as used in this study refers to all the uses of electricity in the rural areas. Thus, the term may include agricultural electrification (use of electricity in agriculture), domestic electrification (use of electricity in the home), and rural industrial electrification (use of electricity in rural industries and village business establishments).
<u>Trapiche</u>	A mill that produces brown sugar.

Weights and Measures

The following weights and measures were used in the study:

Weight Measure

1 arroba	=	25 pounds
1 arroba	=	11.5 kilograms
1 sack	=	100 pounds
1 bulto	=	6 arrobas
1 bulto	=	150 pounds
1 carga	=	2 bultos
1 carga	=	12 arrobas
1 carga	=	300 pounds
1 pucha	=	2 pounds
1 atado	=	2 panelas
1 caneca	=	35 liters
1 quintal	=	100 kilograms

Land Measure

1 hectare	=	10,000 square meters
1 plaza	=	6,400 square meters
1 plaza	=	.64 hectare
1 manzana	=	.64 hectare

Capacity Measure

1 bottle	=	720 grams

NOTE ON CURRENCIES USED

Country	Currency	$ Equivalent
Colombia	peso (Col $)	13.50 = $1.00
Costa Rica	(¢)	
Ecuador	sucre (S/.)	17.82 = $1.00
Nicaragua	cordoba (C $)	7.00 = $1.00

Cooperative
Rural Electrification

1

INTRODUCTION:
FRAMEWORK
FOR ANALYSIS

On May 11, 1964, the U.S. Agency for International Development (AID) approved the world's first international loan for cooperative rural electrification. This loan for development of cooperative electric distribution systems in Colombia was soon followed by others for pilot projects in Nicaragua, Ecuador and Costa Rica. Funds, totaling some $5.8 million, were authorized for development of cooperatives that would eventually distribute electricity to more than 25,000 farms, rural homes, businesses and industries.

Prior to this, rural electrification had not been undertaken to any significant extent--with the exception of Chile--in the Latin American republics. Nor, with the exception of Japan and Taiwan, had rural electrification on a widespread basis been attempted in the Far East. Village electrification programs had been established in some of the developing countries in the Middle East, Asia and Africa, but nowhere in the developing countries had programs adhered to the concept of area coverage--the idea that electric service should be extended to everyone who wants it, no matter how remote his location within a given area. This concept was an

3

integral part of the U.S. rural electrification
program and of the AID-financed pilot rural electrification projects.

PROBLEM SETTING

Data on electricity supply and the rural economy are readily available in the more developed
countries of the world. Growth rates can be established, the needs of different classes of consumers
are known and with the accumulated knowledge of all
other factors likely to influence future demand,
both overall and local planning of rural electrification can be done with reasonable confidence.

This sort of information is not available in
the developing countries. Rural electrification
planning in these countries is hampered by the lack
of relevant history. Actual programs are restrained
by lack of funds. What little electrification there
is outside the areas of major cities has resulted
primarily from domestic demand. It is true that
domestic application of electricity improves living
conditions and provides amenities of great importance in the home. But an even greater consideration in allocation of funds for development projects in low-income countries is that domestic electrification may contribute little or nothing to
productivity of the agricultural enterprise.

Perhaps the most significant justification for
domestic electrification programs is that availability of electricity in the home can be an important factor in preventing migration of population from rural villages to overcrowded towns and
cities. People are less inclined to leave rural
areas in order to enjoy the amenities, real or
imagined, of town living when power for lights,
radio, television, irons and many other appliances
is readily available. In addition, domestic electrification provides the possibility of an indirect
improvement in productivity. By reducing the labor
of housework, electricity makes it possible for

women to spend more time in agricultural work.
Generally, however, the cost of domestic electrification is a charge upon income rather than an ex-
penditure that increases production. Whether the
charge for electricity is greater than for the
forms of energy it replaces depends upon the cost
of fuels, electric rates, equipment costs and other
factors. But in almost all cases, social considerations are the real justification for domestic
electrification.

Rural electrification, in addition to social
considerations, must be concerned with economic results. In order to justify relatively large expenditures of funds, rural electrification which
includes agricultural and industrial as well as domestic application of electricity must lead to an
increased income to cover costs and improve the national level of living. The power available must
be utilized to increase productivity--it must be
used to produce.

FRAMEWORK FOR ANALYSIS

Field studies to develop bench mark data were
conducted in Colombia, Ecuador and Nicaragua during
1964 and 1965. The field study in Costa Rica was
conducted in 1968. Observations from the field
have continued to be reported and a survey of progress in the project areas of all four countries was
conducted in 1970.

The framework for analysis of the projects in
Costa Rica is reported in Chapter 3. For the other
projects, bench mark data and information were obtained in three phases. All three phases involved
field trips by the author to the project areas. A
fourth phase was conducted through completion of
questionnaires by individuals living in the project
areas. Phase I was an organization of the field
study and description of events leading up to organization of the electric cooperative. It attempted to find answers to such questions as: Why

was the particular area selected? Who in the community assumed leadership? Why did members of the
community want electricity.

Phase II was a survey of villages and a sample
of consumers. This period was used to describe the
environment and economic characteristics of the
villages; the intended uses of electricity; present
and future production plans; and basic characteristics of the members. Were members planning to use
electricity only for consumptive purposes, such as
lighting, ventilation, cooking, etc., or were they
also planning to use it for economically productive
purposes, such as motive power for irrigation,
farming tasks and rural industries? What major
problems had the cooperative encountered in its organization?

Phase III was used to describe conditions pri-
or to construction. This phase of the study was
aimed at determining implications for economic and
social development of the area based on conditions
as they existed prior to construction of the rural
electric cooperative. What were the implications
for technical progress, capital accumulation and
institution building? In brief, what were the final implications for promoting economic and social
development in a rural area prior to distribution
of electricity through the institutional arrangement of a cooperative.

Phase IV was a follow-up to determine what
changes had taken place in the rural communities
after energization of the electric distribution
system. Answers were sought to such questions as:
What influence has the use of electric power had on
economic factors? What social changes have taken
place in the community? How many people now have
electricity and how many do not? What are the uses
of electricity? What changes have taken place in
production, population migration, employment, education and industrialization?

The pilot rural electric cooperatives, sponsoring countries, amount of loan funds and estimated potential memberships are listed in Table 1.

TABLE 1

Sponsoring Countries, Loan Funds and Potential Membership
of the Pilot Rural Cooperatives

Name of Cooperative	Sponsoring Country	Loan Funds	Potential Membership
Se-Ca[a]	Colombia	$1,033,600	9,000
Guanacaste) San Marcos) San Carlos)	Costa Rica	3,500,000	13,000
Santo Domingo	Ecuador	650,000	3,300
CAEER #1[b]	Nicaragua	400,000	1,800

Notes: [a]Sevilla-Caicedonia Rural Electric Cooperative.

[b]Tisma Rural Electric Cooperative ("Cooperativa de Abastecimiento de Energia Electrica Rural No. 1").

Source: Loan documents and field surveys.

Emphasis during the field work was placed on the Sevilla-Caicedonia Rural Electric Cooperative (Se-Ca). The major reason was that the project area was more adaptable to analysis. The cooperative comprises the two municipios of Sevilla and Caicedonia for which some data already existed. (A Department is comparable to a state; a Municipio is similar to a county.) It encompasses all villages and rural areas within the municipios.

The Sevilla-Caicedonia project also is relatively isolated from developmental influences outside the municipios. Economic and social changes after the introduction of electricity may be more easily attributed to the project. The cooperative area is located in the northeastern portion of the Department while industry and commerce are concentrated near Cali in the central-southern area. Industrial development in Cali has had little, if any, influence on the development of Sevilla and Caicedonia. The project provided a good testing area and results of operations were to be used to determine applicability of the cooperative mechanism to all rural areas in the Department of Valle.

The Municipios of Sevilla and Caicedonia also present a social challenge to the cooperative organization. Since 1949 they have been considered one of the major areas of Colombia's violence. It was not until the spring of 1964 that the violence was considered to be suppressed. Even today, the Colombian Army maintains control over the area. Thus, the cooperative concept faces a challenge of welding and uniting a community in which there has been social unrest for several years.

Selection of Respondents

Limitations of time and distance prevented an exacting procedure from being followed in selecting samples in the project areas. Terrain is generally rough and roads are in poor condition. A great deal of time is consumed in traveling from one part of a project area to another. Travel is possible

only by jeep, horseback or by walking in many of
the areas.

In addition, houses of the rural residents are
often set back from the road and it is easy to by-
pass many of the farms. Coffee, plantain and shade
trees hide many of the dwellings. Therefore, if a
definite sampling pattern were being followed it
would be impossible to be sure that some of the
farms were not bypassed because they were not noticeable.

The sampling pattern used in the Se-Ca project
area was to conduct the Community Survey at all major communities within the Municipios of Sevilla
and Caicedonia. Fourteen communities, including
the municipal seats of Sevilla and Caicedonia, were
surveyed. Police Inspectors located in each of the
communities were the principal sources of information. The remaining communities included the major
villages in 12 corregimientos. (A corregimiento is
the next smaller administrative unit to a municipio
and is similar to a township in the United States.)
The 12 rural villages surveyed also were designated
distribution points of the rural electric cooperative. These were communities where public lighting
was to be installed.

At the same time a community was surveyed, interviews were conducted at nearby farms. Usually
three or four farmers were interviewed at each distribution point to obtain information for the Consumer Survey. Farms for conducting the interviews
were selected on the basis of location in relation
to the distribution lines. In most of the communities the distribution line passed through the village, permitting farms on both sides of the village
to be interviewed. In others the distribution line
went only as far as the village and interviews
could be conducted on only one side of the village.

Insofar as possible, every other farm in the
direction away from the village was surveyed. If
the farmer was not at home, the survey was conducted

at the next farm. Assistance by personnel familiar
with the area permitted the most efficient use of
transportation and also made it possible to locate
many of the farms that were not visible from the
road. Nevertheless, interviews and travel were
quite time consuming.

Collection of Data

Questionnaires for gathering information in
the field were prepared as follows: (1) Community
Survey, (2) Consumer Survey, (3) Appliance Sales
Survey, (4) Observations Prior to Construction and
(5) Observations after Energization.

Community Survey

The Community Survey form was designed to determine economic and social conditions as they existed before construction of the electric cooperative. Questions seeking this information were
grouped under four major headings: (1) Basic information about the rural community, (2) Environmental characteristics of the community, (3) Economic characteristics of the area and (4) Potential
industrial, agricultural and service activities
with the introduction of electricity.

Major communities within the areas of the ru-
ral electric cooperatives were studies during Phase
II. The 14 communities within the Municipios of
Sevilla and Caicedonia in the Department of Valle
included Alto Colorados, Corozal, Cumbarco, El
Venado, La Cuchilla, Manzanillo, Palomino, San
Antonio, Sevilla, Aures, Caicedonia, Crucero, Mon-
tegrande and Samaria. Communities surveyed in
Nicaragua and Ecuador included Tisma and Santo Do-
mingo, respectively.

Consumer Survey

The Consumer Survey form was designed to determine the immediate uses of electricity by a
sample of potential rural members of the electric

cooperative. From these uses a projection was made of the consumption and cost of electric energy.

The Consumer Survey form was divided into four sections. Section I was used to determine the anticipated use of electricity within one year after energy became available. It also determined what appliances the potential consumers expected to purchase within three years after the cooperative was energized and electric lines were extended to their farms.

Section II of the form contained questions concerning present and future farm production. Section III asked questions that reflected general information about the member-consumer and his farming or rural industry operation.

Extensive interviews were conducted with 80 future rural consumers in the cooperative areas. The schoolteachers were also interviewed to determine if the local schools would use electricity and, if so, for what purpose.

Appliance Sales Survey

The Se-Ca Rural Electric Cooperative was the only one of the four projects that contained retail stores that might sell significant amounts of electrical appliances. Therefore, the Appliance Sales Survey was attempted only in Sevilla and Caicedonia. These two towns are the commercial centers for the two municipios. There are four major retail stores in Sevilla and two in Caicedonia that sell electrical appliances.

The Appliance Sales Survey was used to project the sales of electrical appliances in the cooperative area during the time prior to cooperative rural electrification. Consumers were asked where they intended to purchase their electrical appliances in an attempt to determine what percentage might make their purchases in Sevilla and Caicedonia. Some of the appliances could be purchased

in Armenia, Cali and possibly Bogota and brought
into the cooperative area.

However, it can be assumed that sales of electrical appliances in the towns of Sevilla and
Caicedonia will reflect the use of these appliances
in the cooperative area. It is not believed that
any of the appliances purchased in Sevilla and
Caicedonia will be used outside the cooperative
area. Therefore, one measure of the stimulus of
the electric cooperative to business will be reflected in the amount of sales of electrical appliances in the project area.

Observations Prior to Construction

This form was designed to obtain information
about changes that had taken place or were likely
to occur with the introduction of cooperative electrification.

The form was completed prior to the use of
loan funds for construction of the cooperatives.
It contained implications for (1) resource development, (2) technical progress, (3) capital accumulation and (4) institution-building.

Observations after Energizations

This form was prepared and mailed to people in
the project areas for completion approximately five
years after Phase III of the field study. It was
completed by persons familiar with the economic and
social conditions of the rural areas being serviced
by the electric cooperative. In almost all cases
persons completing the questionnaires had lived in
the areas or had visited the areas periodically
during the five-year period. These observations
were used to record changes that had taken place.

Interpretation of Information

Several factors complicate an evaluation of
returns from using electricity in rural areas.

Benefits cannot be considered entirely from the
standpoint of immediate monetary returns. Returns
may be secondary in nature, that is, they may depend upon the use made of the labor saved. Furthermore, it is difficult to separate the contribution
of electrical equipment from other factors that may
be changing.

Saving labor is less important in enterprises
where a considerable amount of unused family labor
is available. Making work less arduous is more important in enterprises with older operators. Similarly, rural families in different financial positions and possessing different tastes and objectives attach varying degrees of importance to obtaining a given amount of additional leisure. Generally, labor saved during a slack season, such as
the rainy season in some areas or the dry season in
others, has a lower value than it would have during
a harvest season.

Benefits can be evaluated more easily in terms
of individual enterprise situations, keeping in
mind the resources, the objectives and the alternatives that are available. However, the overall
benefits of electricity are more than a summation
of the benefits on individual enterprises. Overall
benefits may include a multiplier effect on the local economy as the result of a specific investment
in electrification. In addition, cooperative rural
electrification may provide indirect benefits that
are impossible to quantify.

Thus, the study did not attempt to quantify
all the effects, but by the case study method it
enumerated advantages and disadvantages that result
in the initial stages of cooperative rural electrification in a developing country. From these advantages and disadvantages, and from a projection
of the intended uses of electricity, conclusions
were drawn.

2

COLOMBIA:
ELECTRIFICATION
AND
RURAL
SOCIALIZATION

STRUCTURE OF THE RURAL ECONOMY

Agriculture is the dominant economic activity
in Colombia despite substantial development of min-
erals and industry. As is true for most countries
in Latin America, approximately half the people
live in rural areas. Farm production provides about
one fourth of the gross national product (GNP) and
earns most of the foreign exchange needed to import
industrial and consumer goods essential to economic
development.

In recent years Colombia has developed an effective national political institution. Under an
agreement between the Liberal and Conservative parties, the national presidency and other posts are
being rotated. The agreement took place after the
economic crisis and overthrow of the Rojas Pinilla
Government in 1957 and is to extend for 16 years
from 1958 to 1974. This agreement greatly allevi-
ated the political instability that was hampering
economic development. Although there are reasons
for concern, the general outlook for political
stability is favorable.

Public education investment has lagged behind
the needs of the economy but the government now
recognizes that an adequate supply of trained personnel is a prerequisite to sustained economic development. The Ministry of Education has reorgan-
ized its planning section and within a few years
it should have a significant impact on education
below the university level. At the university
level, Colombia's educational program should also
have a new look. The Association of Universities
is developing a coordinated university plan for the
country.

Motivation of the country to develop is exem-
plified by initiation of a ten-year development
plan in 1962. Colombia was the first country to
submit such a development program in accordance
with the provisions of the Alliance for Progress.
Land reform is now being carried out along with
other programs to increase and diversify agricultural and industrial production. The country also
has demonstrated its desire to develop by a relatively high rate of domestic savings and investments.

Economic Situation

Since Colombia is primarily a producer and ex-
porter of raw materials, the opportunities to import capital goods and stimulate economic growth
vary with the amount of export earnings.

Coffee is the major foreign exchange earner,
accounting for approximately 70 percent of the
total. Sugar and petroleum also are important export products accounting for about 20 percent.
Petroleum production is expected to increase and
efforts toward diversification are expected to expand exports of other commodities.

An increase of agricultural production is extremely important to Colombia, not only for increasing foreign exchange earnings but also for
supplying the food and raw material requirements
of a rapidly expanding urban population. In recent
years there has been a heavy migration of rural

workers to the cities. The attraction of urban employment and wages, along with violence and banditry
in the rural areas, caused the migration. Substantial unemployment in some of the major cities has
resulted from the influx of rural workers.

Although Colombia's industrial sector has grown
approximately 100 percent during the past ten years,
it has not been able to absorb all of the available
labor. The major portion of the increase in industrial production can be attributed to processed
foods, drugs, clothing, household appliances and
light machinery. Basic materials and heavy equipment must still be imported.

Since 1962 the Colombian Government has taken
steps to restrain operational expenditures, impose
new taxes, increase public savings and reform the
exchange system. While government policies have
caused domestic cost and price increases, they have
also resulted in increased private investment.

GNP has been growing about 5 percent each year.
Population growth, meanwhile, has been increasing
around 3 percent per annum. This means the growth
in per capita product has been around 2 percent annually. Colombian statistics are not precise and
the estimate of growth can be only an approximation;
however, it is a clear indication that real per
capita product has been growing in recent years.

With the favorable outlook for foreign exchange
earnings, with continuing efforts to concentrate resources on the priority needs of the economy, and
with continued financial assistance from abroad, the
prospects for economic growth in Colombia are favorable.

The basic monetary unit of Colombia is the
peso (Col $) divided into 100 centavos. The offi-
cial exchange rate at the time of the study was
13.50 to 1 U.S. dollar.*

_____

*Whenever the dollar sign ($) appears alone or
the word "dollars" is used, they always refer to
U.S. dollars.

General Characteristics

Colombia has a varied terrain and climate. It
occupies an area of 439,530 square miles, equivalent to the areas of France, Spain and Portugal together or is about the combined size of Texas, Okla-
homa, Arkansas and Louisiana.

The country's population in July, 1964, was
16.5 million. By 1970 it had increased to 20 million. About 55 percent of the people live in rural
areas and 52 percent are actively engaged in agriculture. The rapid increase in total population has
caused a substantial increase in both the rural and
urban sectors. But the greatest increase has been
in the urban population. It has been increasing
1 percent about every seven years and the active
agricultural population as a share of the total has
been decreasing in the same proportion.

Most of the population live in the Andes mountains that are formed by three ranges in the western
third of the country. Of this, 2.2 percent are Indian, 20 percent Spanish and other European, 47.8
percent Indian-Spanish, 6 percent African origin
and the remaining 24 percent a mixture of African
with other races.

Colombia's climate is governed primarily by its
terrain. If it were not for the mountains, it would
have an extremely hot climate with slight variations
caused by rains and winds. Thus, the three Andean
ranges result in changes of temperature according to
elevation.

The four general thermal zones are: (1) hot
regions with a mean temperature of 75°F.--0 to
3,280 feet; (2) temperate regions with a mean temperature of not less than 63.5°F.--3,280 to 6,562
feet; (3) cold regions with a mean temperature of
not less than 56.7°F.--6,562 to 9,843 feet; and
(4) paramo (the coldest) regions with a mean temperature of less than 53.6°F.--over 9,843 feet.

In each region there is a different vegetation.
Cacao (cocoa), sugar cane, coconuts, bananas, rice,
sesame, rubber, tobacco, fruits, etc., are cultivated in the hot regions. The temperate regions are
better suited for coffee, vegetables and fruits,
such as oranges, pears, pineapples, tomatoes, etc.
The cold regions produce wheat, barley, potatoes,
vegetables and forest products. Vegetation is
sparse in the paramos.

There are no hot and cold seasons in Colombia,
but the rainy season is often termed winter and the
dry season summer. As a general rule, December,
January, February, March and part of April are the
dry months on the Atlantic coast and the eastern
llanos (plains). Intensive rain prevails during
the remaining months in these areas.

Where the mountain ranges intervene, the seasons are different. In the Cauca Valley, in the
valleys of the Upper Magdalena and in the highlands,
the summer months are January, February, June, July,
August and, in some parts, December. The other
months are the season of rains and drizzles.

Land Use

About 1 out of 3.4 hectares of cultivated land
produces export crops. This leaves about 2.4 million hectares to produce commodities for domestic
consumption. In 1964 there was .15 hectare, or
.375 acre, per person to provide plant products.
In the United States for the same year there was
1.2 acres, more than three times as much.

Colombia's population is increasing at a fast-
er rate than the amount of cultivated land. In
1950 Colombia had an overall average of .6 acre per
person. By 1964 this had fallen to .47. The increase in acreage between 1950 and 1960 was 36 percent. From 1960 to 1964, cultivated land increased
6 percent while the population increased 10.5 percent.

New land areas are being developed principally
in the states of Magdalena and Antioquia in the
north and in Meta in the beginning of the llanos.
In the north the main crops are rice, cotton and
African palm. These new areas are being opened
primarily by men with other businesses who have sufficient credit resources to receive financing.

The majority of Colombian farms are less than
25 acres in size; however, the majority of the farmland is in farms over 250 acres. In 1964 it was estimated 73 percent of the farms were less than 25
acres in size and accounted for 7 percent of the
land. Twenty-four percent of the farms were from
25 to 250 acres in size and accounted for 27 percent
of the land. Farms over 250 acres accounted for 66
percent of the farmland but only 3 percent of all
farms.

Colombian farms primarily are owner-operated.
This includes large owner-operated as well as small
family farms. In 1964 it was estimated 75 percent
of the farms were owner-operated, 15 percent were
operated by squatters and 10 percent were operated
by renters.

Agricultural Production

Colombian agriculture is characterized by a
shortage of cultivated acres and low production per
acre. The result is a high cost of living for the
consumer.

Coffee is the principal commercial crop. Cacao,
wheat, barley, rice, sugar cane, bananas, cotton and
tabacco are also important commercial crops. Corn
is the basic food crop. Together with cassava, potatoes, beans, panela (unrefined brown sugar) and
local fruits, it provides most of the food for the
rural population.

There is about one cow per person in Colombia,
which is a higher ratio than in the United States.
But this is typical of less developed countries and

per capita meat consumption is low. Because corn
is expensive in relation to the price of pork, the
hog population is low. Broilers and fryers sell
rapidly and production is increasing. The price
for live broilers in 1964 was about $.60 per pound.

Coffee is grown on about 25 percent of the
farms and accounts for approximately 20 percent of
the cultivated land. It occupies over 800,000 hectares on 200,000 farms. There are a few large
farms, but the majority are small. Production is
increasing and is about 8 million bags. Prices to
the farmers in 1964 were 735 pesos per 125 kilograms.

Coffee is produced on land that would normally
be in pasture or woods. Therefore, it cannot be
considered as a factor limiting food production.
Bananas and platano (plantain) are often used as
shade for coffee. In this respect, coffee actually
encourages food production.

Tobacco earns about $6.5 million in foreign ex-
change for Colombia each year. Leaf tobacco is at
a record level because of added plantings and improved cultural methods. Production is primarily
in the Departments of Magdalena, Santander and
Boyaca. Production of light air-cured Virginia and
Burley tobacco is also increasing.

Bananas are increasing in importance as a foreign exchange earner. About 12 million stems were
being exported in 1964. The price to the farmer in
1964 was about $.80 per stem. Production is mainly
in the Departments of Magdalena and Antioquia.

Although the government rigorously controls
sugar prices, there is no effort to control panela
prices. Consequently, when the price of panela is
high much of the sugar cane is diverted from sugar
production to production of panela. Panela manufacturers were paying farmers 80 to 90 pesos for
cane in 1964 as compared to 70 pesos by the sugar
manufacturers.

Private capital is continuing to increase sugar output. Large loans have been made to farmers to expand production and a number of mills are increasing their capacity.

Agricultural Problems

Colombia's agriculture has declined about 4 percent in the past ten years in relation to its contribution to GNP. This loss in position for agriculture has been accompanied by gains in all other groups except construction, trade and transportation (see Table 2).

TABLE 2

Index of Domestic Gross Products by Groups
of the Economy in Colombia, 1954 and 1964
(in percent)

Group	1954	1964
Agriculture	33.8	30.0
Fishing	0.1	0.3
Forestry	0.3	0.4
Mining	3.4	3.6
Manufacturing	15.7	19.2
Construction	3.6	3.2
Trade	17.3	14.9
Transportation	6.1	6.0
Communication	0.4	0.7
Electrification	0.6	1.0
Financing	2.2	3.0
Housing	4.7	5.6
Government services	7.0	7.1
Personal services	4.8	5.0
Total:	100.0	100.0

Source: Banco de la Republica, Bogota.

Agriculture's share of GNP in 1964 was about
Col $8 billion, or 30 percent of the total. During
the previous ten years agriculture had increased
its contribution to GNP by more than 30 percent.
The average of all other sectors for the same time
period was more than 50 percent. Thus, agriculture
is a declining industry in Colombia.

One of the major factors accounting for the
slow development in agriculture and its relative
decline in the share of GNP is that there is not
enough land in cultivation. Per capita land in cultivation is less than one third that of the United
States. In addition, about 27 percent of the land
produces export crops. The increased acreage in
recent years has been about 1.7 percent per year,
much less than population growth.

Low yields is another important factor causing
agriculture's decline. Wheat, which is produced on
valuable land, yields about 10 bushels per acre.
Corn, which is next to coffee in acreage and value,
normally yields 10 to 14 bushels to the acre. On
the other hand, cotton, tobacco, potato and soybean
yields are fairly high relative to other less developed countries.

Lack of cultivated land and low yields point
out other problems. There is a scarcity of culti-
vable land near population centers. Transportation
is either nonexistent or very expensive. There is
a problem of capital and technical knowledge in the
rural areas. Farmers do not use improved seeds and
fertilizers. There is a lack of conservation measures. And the general area of marketing presents
a sizable problem. In the marketing centers there
is an uncertainty of supply, lack of warehousing,
quality is poor and there are pricing and information problems.

Development Programs

Colombia's varied resources provide the country with a great potential for agricultural production. Many crops grown in the United States can be

grown in Colombia because of the wide range in elevation in the western half of the country. In addition, many tropical crops that cannot be grown in
the United States can be grown in Colombia. Also,
the long growing season makes it possible in many
cases to grow two crops in one year.

With the vast potential for agriculture, Colombia lacks only the programs and the people for developing the potential. Agrarian reform--including
credit, development of livestock and basic resources,
diversification of agriculture, marketing, agricultural training and research, national agricultural
planning and cooperative development--is being emphasized to develop Colombia's agricultural potential.

.Agrarian reform in Colombia includes not only
land and water resource development but also taxa-
tion, credit, expansion of operations of small
farms, subdivision of large holdings, voluntary expansion of agriculture into new land areas and improvement of land title and contract law.

Colombia has extensive undeveloped resources
in both land and water. Development of these resources will make it possible to greatly increase
agricultural production. Proper use of land and
water is one of the basic requirements for economic
development. Proper planning of uses of water for
domestic, industrial, irrigation and hydroelectric
purposes is increasingly important with the development of the country. Proper planning of land use
is just as important and can be of great significance in the overall development of a country.

Per capita consumption of meat in Colombia is
low and expansion of the livestock industry is essential to meet nutritional needs. In addition,
expansion of livestock exports can help increase
needed foreign exchange earnings. The program to
increase livestock production and efficiency is being emphasized through development loans. High
priority will be given toward promoting the export
of beef.

Diversification is essential to the agricultural economy of Colombia. Because of Colombia's varied resources the possibilities for diversification are virtually unlimited. Much work by various organizations and federations already has been accomplished. Work has been undertaken to develop African palm, to make Colombia self-sufficient in rubber and to determine the potential for production of various types of tropical fruit.

It is well known that marketing has been neglected in Colombia. One of the country's biggest problems is in transporting the products from the farm to the market. Colombia's terrain adds to the problems in constructing adequate means of transportation. Perishable produce is often damaged while being transported on the rough roads.

Other areas of marketing that need improvement and where development programs are being directed include packaging, grading, wholesale market efficiency, reduction of middlemen and excessive margins, processing, slaughtering, price ceilings, price supports, storage, retail markets, and controls on exports and imports.

Development programs are also aimed at training agricultural technicians. Investments in education, research and training pay some of the greatest dividends in the long-run development of a country. There is a need in Colombia for more trained personnel in animal science, farm management, marketing, land development, extension and rural institutional organization.

Programs are now underway to strengthen the cooperative movement in Colombia. Through the Colombian Association of Cooperatives, assistance is being given to new cooperatives and member cooperatives in management and training problems. Efforts are being continued to solve the need of adequate financing for developing cooperatives.

Other programs are underway to develop and strengthen rural cooperatives in the fields of

agricultural marketing, rural electrification and
agricultural supply.

RURAL DEVELOPMENT FACTORS
IN THE DEPARTMENT OF VALLE

The Department of Valle is located in the
southwestern part of Colombia. It is one of 18 departments in the country. Cali, the capital of
Valle, is 352 miles from the Panama Canal and located on the Pan American Highway. Because of its
geographic location, Cali serves as the trade center for the western section of Colombia. Location
of the Department of Valle in Colombia is shown in
Map 1.

Natural and Human Resources

The Department of Valle encompasses 20,430
square kilometers (7,888 square miles), slightly
larger than the state of New Jersey. Excluding 743
square kilometers (287 square miles) making up the
Municipios of Sevilla and Caicedonia, there are
19,687 square kilometers in the 40 remaining municipios. Topographic, climatic, meteorologic, bio-
logic and economic characteristics for the 40 municipios outside the pilot project area are quite
similar.[1] This area represents 1.7 percent of the
area of Colombia and 96.4 percent of the area of
the Department of Valle.

Among the 40 municipios, Buenaventura has the
largest area with 5,953 kilometers accounting for
almost one third of the Department, or 30 percent
of the area of the 40 municipios. The smallest is
Alcala with only 30 square kilometers.

Colombia is located in the tropical zone, but
the climate of the country varies with the altitude.
Cali is located at 3,000 feet above sea level and
at the edge of a 1 million acre valley, which is
embraced by two branches of the Andes Cordilleras
(mountain ridges). Consequently the climate of the

MAP 1
The Department of Valle

ATLANTIC OCEAN

PANAMA

VENEZUELA

PACIFIC OCEAN

COLOMBIA

VALLE

BRAZIL

ECUADOR

PERU

valley has a subtropical nature, being very similar
to that of Florida. Relative humidity in Cali aver-
ages 69 percent and the average temperature is 75°F.

The main river that passes from north to south
through the valley has a flow of 10,000 gallons per
minute at Cali. In addition, ground water suitable
for irrigation and industrial purposes is available
at reasonable depths through most of the valley.

In the valley of the Cauca River between the
central and western mountain chain there is a rich
agricultural area approximately 200 kilometers long,
30 kilometers wide and 1,000 meters above sea level.
The soils of the valley are more or less uniform--
black in color, compact structure, clay texture
with a great quantity of organic matter and with a
thickness of about 50 centimeters.

The clayish and compact character of the soil
impedes the permeability and aeration of the land
with the consequent oxidation of the organic material that it possesses. These characteristics and
irregular precipitation prevent roots from growing
deeper than 20 centimeters. This is also the usual
depth of plowing.

Electric power supply is balanced between
thermo and hydro plants. There is presently an installed capacity of close to 1 million kilowatts.
An additional million kilowatts of hydro power has
been surveyed for future expansions.

Immediately after its inception in 1954 the
Department's power authority, CVC (Corporacion
Autonoma Regional de Cauca) embarked on a large-
scale program to solve the existing lag in the supply of electric power. The problem was to be
solved through integrated projects of generation,
high-voltage transmission and distribution. CVC
objectives are a large power availability in the
whole Department with a guarantee of reliability in
service and dependability in generating capacity.
Empresas Municipales de Cali distributes electric

power to the municipalities of Cali, Humbo, Puerto
Tejada and Jasmundi through a mixed generating system.

As a complement to generation projects, CVC is
installing a wide high-voltage transmission network
that will reach the major centers throughout the Department. Distribution systems will be connected
to the main network and their operation will be in
charge of agencies in the various localities, with
the participation of CVC. Areas located too far
away from the grid system to make connection possible will be served by power plants constructed
by CVC.

Although heavy industry in the area depends on
coal as a basic fuel, oil products are also available from nearby areas. Local coal reserves are
large enough to cover the needs of the area for
many generations. Forest resources on the Pacific
seaboard are also plentiful. Cement and other construction materials are produced locally.

The population of the Department of Valle in
July, 1964 was 1.7 million. Approximately 60 percent lived in the urban areas. Cali, with a population of about 650,000 in 1964, has become one of
the three largest cities in Colombia--1970 population was approximately 1 million.

Within the state there are five other major
cities with more than 80,000 inhabitants each.
These cities are interconnected with the capital
by paved roads.

Productive Organization

The Cauca Valley produces all of the sugar,
all of the soybeans, and one third of the cotton
grown in Colombia. In addition, it is becoming one
of Colombia's major industrial centers.

Natural conditions have made the Department of
Valle exceptionally favorable for agricultural

activities. The extension of useful land, excellent
conditions of fertility, variation in altitude and
favorable topographic characteristics for agricultural mechanization are all factors pointing to the
huge potential of the Cauca Valley as a source of
food and fiber supply to other parts of Colombia
and for export.

These characteristics have led to different regional activities within the Cauca Valley. Coffee
is grown in the northern mountainous areas, mostly
for export. Basic foods such as corn, rice and
beans are sold for domestic consumption. Raw materials such as sugar cane, bagasse,* cotton and soybeans are used in manufacturing activities. Also,
complementary export sources have been created in
recent years through the disposal of sugar and cotton surpluses.

There are roughly 300,000 hectares under cultivation, 870,000 hectares in pasture and 150,000
covered by forests. CVC programs of flood control,
land reclamation and cultivation are progressively
changing the land-use pattern.

Census data indicate that 10 percent of the
area under cultivation was in farms ranging from 10
to 100 hectares; and 60 percent in farms larger
than 100 hectares. Eleven percent of the total cultivated area was in farms larger than 100 hectares.

Sugar production and processing involves both
agricultural and manufacturing activities. It is
the most important industry in Valle in terms of
employment, payroll, value added and investment.
Practically the entire sugar production of Colombia
takes place in the Cauca Valley. Domestic consumption has been the traditional outlet, but export
possibilities have developed in recent years. It
is estimated some 40,000 hectares of sugar cane

---

*Part of sugar cane left after juice has been
taken out.

supply the sugar mills and the remainder serves the
panela industry. Total employment is over 17,000
workers distributed among sugar refineries, <u>trapiches</u>
(mills that produce brown sugar) and cane fields.
The land of the Cauca Valley, together with the
Peruvian coastal strip and some Indonesian areas,
are the only parts of the world where there is no
sugar season limiting yields and continuity in operation.

The National Federation of Coffee Growers estimates that 13 percent of Colombia's coffee crop
originates in the Cauca Valley. Production is usually more than 1 million bags (60 kilos each).
Sevilla, Caicedonia, Trujillo and other northern
municipios located on the slopes of the central
range of the Andes, are the leading production
areas. A very large proportion of the crop goes to
the Armenian coffee market for packing and branding.

Cotton cultivation in the Cauca Valley has
grown substantially in recent years. Cotton exports
to Europe and Japan have been made through barter
arrangements. These shipments "have made possible
the importation of cars and other merchandise for
which dollar resources were not previously sufficient."[2]

Grain production also is important, with corn
accounting for about 20 percent of the value of
agricultural production in the Cauca Valley. Irreg-
ularity of rain is one of the principal factors affecting corn production. Industrial demand in Colombia has strongly stimulated the growth of soybeans in the valley.

In addition to corn and soybeans, rice and
beans are grown in the Cauca Valley on a large
scale. Output is primarily locally consumed, but
some is shipped to other departments.

About 20 percent of the value of Colombia's
industrial goods are produced in Valle. The importance of industrial production within the Department

and the place of the Department within the country
as an industrial producer have been increasing in
recent years.

The principal manufactured goods in Valle include textiles, tires, cement, food products, metal
products, paper, chemicals and pharmaceuticals,
milk products, alcohol, rum and sugar. In addition
to Cali, manufacturing centers in Valle include
Palmira, Tulua, Buga and Cartago.

There are 40 major internationally known manu-
facturing firms established in Cali. These firms
include Union Carbide, Goodyear, U.S. Rubber, Borden
Chemical, International Paper, Container Corporation,
Celanese, Alcan, Corn Products, Colgate, Gillette,
Squibb, Sears Roebuck, W. R. Grace and Hoechst.

The Pacific seaport of Buenaventura is located
80 miles from Cali. It is the most active harbor in
Colombia, serving approximately 1,000 oceangoing
ships every year. Between Cali and the seaboard is
a highway and railroad line, and a modern high-speed
highway is almost finished. Substantial harbor improvements are also underway.

Within the state limits the main roads are
paved. The Pan American Highway, which goes through
the Cauca Valley, extends all the way south to Ar-
gentina. The capital of the state is interconnected
both by rail and road with the major cities of Colombia. The railroad system is equipped with diesel
engine locomotives.

Cali is also one of the most active airway hubs
of Colombia. Its airport registers 460,000 passengers per year and the trend of growth of traffic is
the highest in the country.

Within a range of 300 miles from Cali there are
11 million people. This is nearly 70 percent of the
population of Colombia and the areas where per capita income is the highest in the country.

Technology

Light tools traditionally employed in the Department, such as machetes, hoes, etc., are gradual-
ly being replaced by tractors and other equipment.
In the Department, as is general in Colombia, the
farm labor force is underutilized since the supply
is greater than the demand. This has caused a reduction in the level of wages for farm workers.

Tractors are generally used in the Department
for preparing the soil for rice, corn, sugar cane,
cotton and other crops of less importance in the
region.

The reason for the higher amount of mechanization in Cali, 83 percent of the total, is because
the average size of the farms is larger. This permits greater use of agricultural machinery.

Inadequate exploitation of the land is one of
the most important factors affecting agriculture in
Valle. On most of the small and medium sized farms
there is little use of improved seeds. Fertilizer
is not used and the soil is not maintained by crop
rotation. Insecticides and fungicides are not used
and farm management is poor.

Especially on the small and medium sized farms
it is necessary to develop a program that will
change the antiquated farming practices. Modern
farm technology practices in the Cauca Valley could
result in a substantial increase in agricultural
production.

Capital and Credit

There is no information concerning capital investments in agriculture in the Department. A study
of the municipios of Roldanillo, La Union and Toro,
however, showed the average amount of capital invested in farms of less than 1 hectare to be Col
$4,125. For farms from 1 hectare to 5 hectares the

investment went up to Col $18,015, and the amount
continued to increase with the size of the farm.
Farms of more than 100 hectares had a capital investment of more than Col $1 million.

Facilities for credit in Valle is the principal problem facing the agricultural sector. Main
sources of credit for farms include the Caja Agraria
(Agricultural Bank), commercial banks and more recently INCORA (Instituto Colombiano de la Reforma
Agraria), the land reform agency.

The average value of loans at the time of the
field study was Col $5,570. The amount of interest
varied with the size of the loan and the period of
time. Loans up to Col $5,000 generally were as fol-
lows: short-term--8 percent annually; medium term--
10 percent; and long-term--12 percent. Loans for
more than Col $5,000 were generally as follows:
short-term--9 percent; medium term--11 percent; and
long-term--12 percent.[3]

The length of loans varied from 1 year to 12
years. The maximum amount for short-term loans was
Col $150,000 and the maximum for medium terms was
Col $300,000.

As a part of the national land reform program,
INCORA established five centers of credit for small
farmers in Valle. The centers, located in Palmira,
Candelaria, Cerrito, Florida and Roldanillo, are
for farmers who cannot gain access to credit through
normal sources.

Through the supervised credit program INCORA is
trying to develop cooperatives, irrigation, increase
the production of dairy cows, hogs and chickens and
increase the use of agricultural equipment, seeds
and fertilizer.

While the Department is emphasizing agricultural development it is placing even more emphasis
on industrial development. It anticipates that new
industries will bring capital to the area. This in

turn will have a positive effect on the local
economy.

Basic industries in Cali are exempt from paying income tax for the first ten years of operation.
Municipalities near Cali offer low tax rates, or
complete exemption of property tax and other municipal taxes. No income tax is collected at the department or local level.

Institutional Structure

There are several public and private organizations in the Department that influence agriculture.
Private organizations represent specific areas of
interest within the agricultural sector. These organizations provide an important link between the
agricultural producers and the government. Some of
the organizations, such as the National Federation
of Coffee Growers, also provide direct assistance
for the producers.

Important private organizations include:
Almacenes Generales de Deposito del INA y Caja
Agraria S.A. (INAGRARIO); Asociacion Nacional de
Cultivadores de Cana de Azucar (ASOCANA); Asocia-
cion de Porcicultores; Banco Ganadero; Federacion
Nacional de Algodoneros; Federacion Nacional de
Cafeteras; Federacion Nacional de Arroceros; Fondo
Ganadero del Valle del Cauca; Sociedad de Agricul-
tores y Ganaderos del Valle del Cauca; and Sociedad
de Agricultores Japoneses (SAJA).

Most of the public organizations are dependent
on national policies and programs. Public organizations influencing agriculture in Valle include:
Caja de Credito Agrario, Industrial y Minero; Centro Nacional de Investigaciones Agricolas; Centro
de Formacion Profesional e Investigacion Agricola;
Instituto de Fomento Algondonero (IGA); Secretaria
de Agricultura y Ganaderia del Valle del Cauca;
Zona Agropecuaria del Valle del Cauca (Ministerio
de Agricultura); and Corporacion Autonoma Regional
del Cauca (CVC).

There are several different types of cooperatives in Colombia. Consumer and credit cooperatives
are the most numerous. But cooperatives play a
small role in Colombia. Less than 2 percent of the
population belong to approximately 525 cooperative
organizations. In a predominantly agricultural
economy, cooperative members represent about 0.4
percent of the rural population.[4]

The Cauca Valley has approximately 100 cooperatives and about 10 percent of them are agricultural.
While roughly 1 percent of the population in the Department belongs to cooperatives, less than 1 percent are members of agricultural cooperatives.

The Federacion de Cooperativas del Valle del
Cauca was organized to provide assistance to affili-
ated firms in Valle. Although it is a relatively
young organization, it has had some success in promoting and assisting the cooperative movement in
the Department.

CVC was the first regional authority (established in 1954) created by the Government of Colombia with autonomous powers from traditional government branches. It has some general planning lines
common to similar agencies such as the Tennessee
Valley Authority. Its main purpose is the planning
and implementation of a development program in the
Cauca Valley region embodying flood control, land
reclamation, agricultural projects and generation
of electricity, high-voltage transmission and distribution of electric power.

The principal internal source of funds of CVC
is a surtax levied on real estate in the Department
at an annual rate of 3 pesos per thousand on as-
sessed land value. Property owners with less than
100,000 pesos of capital are exempted. A complementary financial source is provided by 50 percent of
revenue from an existing excise tax on domestic alcohol beverages.

SOCIOECONOMIC CONDITIONS IN THE
PROJECT AREA

For political and administrative purposes, the Municipios of Sevilla and Caicedonia are divided in corregimientos. Each corregimiento is administered by an Inspector de Policia Departmental. The Police Inspectors are appointed by the governor of the Department of Valle.

Usually there is one rural village in each corregimiento that is substantially larger than the other villages. This is the village where the police inspector establishes his headquarters and performs the functions of his office.

Construction plans for the rural electric cooperative provided for electricity in 12 of the 23 corregimientos making up the Municipios of Sevilla and Caicedonia. Later, after the cooperative had established operations successfully, distribution lines were to be constructed in the remaining corregimientos. Location of the Municipios of Sevilla and Caicedonia in the Department of Valle is shown in Map 2.

In Sevilla there are 16 corregimientos, while there are 7 in Caicedonia. Corregimientos in Sevilla include: Alegrias, Ceballal, *Coloradas, *Corozal, *Cumbarco, *El Venado, La Astelia, *La Cuchilla, La Estrella, *Manzanillo, Miraflores, *Palomino, *San Antonio, San Marcos, Totoro and Tres Esquinas. Corregimientos in Caicedonia include: *Aures, Burila, *El Crucero, Rivera, *Montegrande, *Samaria and San Gerardo.

The symbol (*) represents the corregimientos where the electric distribution lines of the cooperative were to be constructed in the initial phase. These also are the corregimientos where the community surveys were conducted. In almost all cases the police inspector of the corregimiento was the

MAP 2

Location of Sevilla-Caicedonia Cooperative
in the Department of Valle

CALDAS

CHOCO

CAICEDONIA

SEVILLA

BUENAVENTURA

DEPARTMENT OF VALLE

TOLIMA

PACIFIC OCEAN

CALI

CAUCA

38

primary source of information. This information
was often supplemented with information obtained
from the Junta de Accion Comunal.

Geography and Climate

The project area encompasses 743 square kilometers (287 square miles), an area almost five
times as large as Washington, D.C. The Municipio
of Sevilla with 557 square kilometers is three
times as large as the Municipio of Caicedonia with
186 square kilometers.

Temperature in the area is considered moderate.
Altitude in most of the project area is between
1,000 and 2,000 meters above sea level. The region
is characterized by relatively high humidity and
has an annual rainfall of 1,700 millimeters (66.9
inches), which is especially favorable for coffee
growing. Rainfall is approximately the same in
both municipios.

The Municipio of Sevilla is a mountainous area
that varies in altitude from 1,100 to 3,500 meters.
Only in three areas in the municipio--La Astelia,
La Estrella and El Venado--are there small valleys.
The city of Sevilla is at 1,598 meters in altitude.

The average temperature in Sevilla is 64°F.
Temperature variation throughout the year is slight.
During the year there are two rainy periods and two
dry periods. The first rainy period is in March,
April, May and part of June. The second rainy
period begins in September and lasts through October, November and the first part of December. The
other months are the dry periods.

The Municipio of Caicedonia is also located in
a rugged mountainous area. Some of the northern
part of the Municipio of Caicedonia is less mountainous and more favorable to cultivated crops than
any other sector in the project area. This is the
area where most of the sugar cane is grown within
the cooperative boundaries.

The altitude of Caicedonia is 1,100 meters and the average temperature is 79°F. Thus, the city of Caicedonia is lower than Sevilla and the temperature is higher. The rainy periods and the dry months are the same in Caicedonia as in Sevilla.[5]

Population and Education

The ethnic composition of the population in Sevilla and Caicedonia is based on families that have migrated to the area from Antioquia. Their ancestry is of the old Spanish families that settled in the western part of the Department of Antioquia. They were known for their adventuresome spirit and their desire for conquests. They reputedly had a strong love for work.

Population in the Municipio of Sevilla in 1964 numbered 44,395, while Caicedonia had 28,117. The rural population in Sevilla makes up 40 percent of the municipio's total population and in Caicedonia it accounts for 42 percent of the municipio's total. The population of each of the villages surveyed was estimated and an opinion was obtained as to the population movement. The results are shown in Table 3.

Those villages where there was immigration had been in some of the hardest hit areas by Colombia's violence. Persons interviewed in the villages said farm owners were moving back into the area since the Colombian Army had suppressed the violence. They said there was more tranquility in the area now and people were returning to farm the land.

The only reason for emigration in some of the other villages was that the people were going to larger cities or other areas to seek work.

The number of schools and students in the Municipios of Sevilla and Caicedonia in 1960 are shown in Table 4.

TABLE 3

Estimated Village Population and Population Movement in Electric Cooperative Area, March, 1965

Village	Estimated Population	Population Movement
Sevilla:		
Coloradas	180	Immigration
Corozal	490	Emigration
Cuchilla	90	Emigration
Cumbarco	350	Stable
Manzanillo	200	Emigration
Palomino	130	Stable
San Antonio	600	Stable
Venado	300	Stable
Caicedonia:		
Aures	200	Immigration
Crucero	160	Immigration
Montegrande	180	Immigration
Samaria	260	Stable

Source: Community Survey.

TABLE 4

Urban and Rural Schools and Students in Sevilla and Caicedonia, 1960

Municipio	Urban	Rural	Total
Schools:			
Sevilla	10	37	47
Caicedonia	3	7	10
Students:			
Sevilla	3,467	1,501	4,968
Caicedonia	2,453	636	3,089

Source: Department of Statistics, Valle.

Primary rural schools only teach two or three years. Less than 20 percent of the students in rural areas beginning primary school complete the course. In the Municipio of Sevilla there are two colegios or high schools, one for boys and one for girls. There were no secondary schools in the rural areas. In addition, there were various private schools in Sevilla.

Some adult education programs had been sponsored in Sevilla from time to time by SENA (Servicio Nacional de Aprendizaje) and the Sevilla Coffee Cooperative. In the rural areas a course for farm managers had been given at Palomino by SENA. The same type of course was being planned in Venado; however, in none of the other villages had there been any type of education program for adults.

In Caicedonia a course in reading had been given for adults, both during the day and at night. In the rural areas of the Municipio there were no adult education programs. In Samaria, two months before the survey, a course for adults had been organized but was discontinued because of lack of sufficient light. It was also in Samaria that the Cooperativa de Caficultores de Caicedonia had built the primary school and was paying the teacher.

Estimated literacy levels, number of primary schools and number of teachers for the villages are shown in Table 5. The estimated average level of literacy for the cooperative area was 54 percent. For the 19 Latin American republics the level of literacy in 1962 was 55 percent, while literacy for the entire country of Colombia was 62 percent.

Community Welfare and Leadership

Sevilla and Caicedonia are lagging socially and economically in comparison to other communities in the Cauca Valley. Lack of modern improvements that have been initiated in other municipios have added to the social unrest.

TABLE 5

Estimated Literacy, Number of Schools and
Number of Instructors in Rural Villages
in Cooperative Area, March, 1965

Rural Village	Estimated Literacy (in percent)	Number of Schools	Number of Instructors
Sevilla:			
Coloradas	75	2	2
Corozal	50	1	2
Cuchilla	25	2	2
Cumbarco	50	2	2
Manzanillo	25	2	2
Palomino	25	2	2
San Antonio	50	2	4
Venado	75	1	1
Caicedonia:			
Aures	75	2	4
Crucero	75	1	1
Montegrande	50	2	2
Samaria	75	1	2

Source: Community Survey.

Violence, which has plagued the rural areas of
Colombia since 1949, has been particularly prominent in the areas of Sevilla and Caicedonia.   In
the beginning the struggle between Conservatives
and Liberals was an important·cause of violence.
But this aspect disappeared with the political
coalition and banditry became the major cause of
violence.

The importance of violence and rural unrest
is brought into focus in a descriptive account by
Alonso Moncada.[6] In his book about the violence,
Moncada states that it is impossible to calculate

exactly the number that have been killed. From
1949 to 1963, General Alberto Ruiz Novoa, former
Minister of War, estimated that more than 300,000
people were killed in Colombia's violence.

In 1960 and 1961, the years for which figures
are available, the Department of Valle had the highest number of deaths of all Departments caused by
the violence with 739 and 965 for the respective
years. A study of these two years showed that the
number of deaths of Conservatives was approximately
equal to that of Liberals.[7]

By 1964 the efforts of the national and state
governments had suppressed the violence. Roadblocks
operated by the Colombian Army were scattered
through the electric cooperative area. While the
Army has suppressed violence in the cooperative
area, there still is social unrest. If the Colombian Army were to be withdrawn from the Sevilla-
Caicedonia area, it is quite likely that the former
rate of violence activities would occur once again.

Data obtained from the National Army in Sevilla
showed deaths from violence in the electric cooperative area between January, 1963 and December, 1964.[8]
This information is reported in Table 6.

A major portion of the unrest is caused by the
low level of living. Until economic and social conditions are improved in the area, violence can only
be suppressed and not eliminated. The unrest provides a favorable climate for insurgency. Agitation
by extremist groups was prominent during organization of the cooperative.

Community facilities for obtaining water and
drainage were extremely limited. Sevilla obtained
water through a gravity system from the Popal River,
which is located about 1 kilometer east of the city.
The water was not potable. There were drainage
facilities in the city of Sevilla but not in the
barrios (suburbs).

TABLE 6

Deaths from Violence in Sevilla
and Caicedonia, 1963 and 1964

	1963	1964
Sevilla:		
Soldiers	2	8
Civilians	39	10
Bandits	12	9
Caicedonia:		
Soldiers	--	--
Civilians	50	9
Bandits	12	15
Total	115	51

Source: Colombian National Army, Sevilla.

None of the rural villages except San Antonio
had drainage facilities. Coloradas had an aqueduct
carrying water from a storage tank built by the
Federation of Coffee Growers. Corozal also had an
aqueduct constructed by the Coffee Federation.
Cuchilla obtained water through an aqueduct from a
tank near Manzanillo, 7 kilometers away. Cumbarco
obtained water from a nearby stream. The tank stor-
ing water for Palomino was located 4 kilometers
from the village.

San Antonio had a drainage system extending for
four blocks through the main part of the village.
Water was obtained from a pump located 3 kilometers
outside the village. It was managed by the Junta
de Accion Comunal. Venado had an aqueduct constructed by the Coffee Federation.

Caicedonia had a limited drainage system in the central part of the city. Water was obtained from a large storage tank outside the city. It was not potable. None of the rural villages in Caicedonia had drainage facilities and none had potable water. Aures obtained water through an aqueduct constructed by the National Federation of Coffee Growers. Crucero and Montegrande also had aqueducts built by the National Federation. Samaria had an aqueduct but it was in very bad condition and a study was being made by the National Federation to build a new one.

Thus, nowhere in the area where the electric cooperative was to be constructed was there a source of potable water. Most of the rural population, however, considered the water potable and freely drank the water without it being purified.

In 1960, only 47 percent of Colombia's total population had potable water and 34 percent sewage service. More than 60 percent of the deaths were caused by gastroenteritis infections attributable to impure water. Colombia's death rate of 12.6 per thousand is one of the highest in Latin America.

One of the principal problems hindering development of adequate health and sanitation services in Colombia is the lack of trained medical personnel. In 1964 Colombia had only 4.4 physicians, .6 graduate nurses and 1.4 nursing auxiliaries per 10,000 population, which is considered well below minimum standards.[9]

The number of trained medical personnel in the rural electric cooperative area was even at a lower level. In 1964 there were 1.04 physicians per 10,000 population in the Municipio of Sevilla, less than one fourth of the national average.

At the time of the survey, Sevilla had 7 medical doctors, 3 dentists, 12 pharmacists and several nurses and midwives. There was one hospital in the city with 25 beds for children, 28 beds for men, 38 beds for women, 10 beds for obstetrics and 8 beds for maternity cases. In the rural areas there was a health station in San Antonio and another was being planned in Venado.

San Antonio had one midwife with a title. Corozal had two midwives without titles and this was the extent of medical facilities in the areas surveyed in Sevilla. Except for Corozal, people from the rural villages went to Sevilla for medical attention. By using the railroad, the people in Corozal could go to Armenia and Zarzal.

Caicedonia had 6 doctors, 2 dentists, 12 nurses, 4 midwives and 5 pharmacists. It had one general hospital. In the rural areas, Aures had 1 midwife and this was the extent of medical facilities in the cooperative area in Caicedonia.

In Sevilla the community center was the Casa Municipal. In Coloradas the community center was the kiosko or caseta. The community center in Corozal had collapsed and the village had not built a new one. In Cuchilla and Cumbarco the schools served as the community centers. Manzanillo had built a new community center, Casa Accion. Palomino also had a special building serving as the community center. San Antonio did not have any community center and Venado used the office building of the Police Inspector for the community center.

The community center in Caicedonia was the municipal building. In Aures the school served as the community center while Crucero used the building of the Police Inspector. Montegrande used the school building and Samaria used a kiosko.

The only cooperative serving the entire electric cooperative area was the Cooperativa de Caficultores. In Sevilla there was also a Cooperativa de Transportes. In addition, Sevilla had several religious organizations and social service groups as well as four social clubs.

A Cooperativa de Caficultores de Caicedonia
Ltda. had recently been organized in the Municipio
of Caicedonia. Also, there was a Comite de Cafe-
teros functioning to provide service and extension
education to the coffee growers. In addition, there
were two service clubs organized in Caicedonia.

Juntas de Accion Comunal had been organized or
were in the process of being organized in most of
the corregimientos at the time of the survey. Peace
Corps Volunteers had been instrumental in organizing
the Juntas in the barrios of Sevilla and in some of
the surrounding rural areas.

Most of the houses in the rural villages consisted of a kitchen, a living room and one or more
bedrooms. They were usually painted with a mixture
of lime, sand and water.

The types of material used in construction
varied slightly from one village to another. Tile
was used almost altogether for roof construction in
the 12 villages. In some cases zinc was used but
tile was the predominant material (see Tables 7
and 8).

Sevilla and Caicedonia are governed by Municipal Councils. Each Council consists of 16 members
elected by the population of the Municipio. Several factors, such as transportation, communication
and education, contribute to the fact that almost
always the council is made up of members living in
the population center.

The mayors of Sevilla and Caicedonia are military personnel. They were appointed rather than
elected. In both Sevilla and Caicedonia the mayors
were Army Captains.

Generally, those persons in the various rural
communities serving as presidents of the Juntas de
Accion Comunal and the Police Inspector of the
corregimientos surveyed were civilians except in
Aures. This had been one of the worst of the violence areas and the military was performing the
functions of the police inspector.

TABLE 7

Percentage of Houses in Rural Villages
with Different Types of Flooring,
March, 1965

	Type of Flooring		
Village	Concrete	Wood	Dirt
Sevilla:			
Coloradas	--	80	20
Corozal	20	80	--
Cuchilla	2	98	--
Cumbarco	--	75	25
Manzanillo	--	100	--
Palomino	10	90	--
San Antonio	10	90	--
Venado	10	85	5
Caicedonia:			
Aures	5	95	--
Crucero	50	50	--
Montegrande	20	70	10
Samaria	--	100	--

Source: Community Survey.

TABLE 8

Percentage of Houses in Rural Villages
with Different Types of Walls,
March, 1965

	Type of Wall		
Village	Wood	Brick	Mud
Sevilla:			
Coloradas	90	--	10
Corozal	20	--	80
Cuchilla	--	2	98
Cumbarco	--	--	100
Manzanillo	--	50	50
Palomino	70	5	25
San Antonio	3	7	90
Venado	10	20	70
Caicedonia:			
Aures	5	35	60
Crucero	--	50	50
Montegrande	15	15	70
Samaria	10	--	90

Source: Community Survey.

Among the 12 junta presidents in the rural villages, all were male and all but one were farmers. The exception was the junta president in San Antonio who operated a small general store. More than half of the junta presidents were 40 years of age or less. Community leadership in the project area in 1965 is shown in Table 9.

Transportation and Communication

The only hard-surface road in the project area was the Pan American Highway, which passed through the cities of Sevilla and Caicedonia. Commodities produced in the area could be transported to the major markets by trucking them over this highway.

Transportation away from the Pan American Highway in the cooperative area had to be by jeep, horseback or on foot. A railroad passed through the northern edge of the area and within 6 kilometers of the city of Caicedonia. There were no navigable rivers, ports or airports in either municipio.

In both Sevilla and Caicedonia there were several companies providing transportation for passengers and for cargo. Taxi service in the cities was by automobile, but taxi service in the country was by jeep. Two companies, Transportes San Luis and Transportes Octavio Gutierrez, provided transportation for cargo in Sevilla. Five companies, Flota Cincuentenario, Tax Tres de Mayo, Trans-Venado, Trans-San Antonio, and Trans-Dinamarca, provided transportation for passengers in Sevilla. These companies were assigned specific zones in the municipio. For transportation outside the municipio, there were two companies, La Flota Magdalena and Expreso Palmira.

Sevilla had several means of communication. There was a radio station in the city. It had an automatic telephone system and a telegraph system. Television reception from Bogota was fairly good. Sevilla also had two weekly newspapers and received daily newspapers from larger cities for distribution.

TABLE 9

Leadership in the Electric Cooperative Area, March, 1965

Community	Name of Leader	Position	Age	Occupation
Sevilla	Sarafin Aranzazu U.	Council President	62	Businessman
	Carlos Gamba	Mayor	45	Army Captain
Coloradas	Jose Alfredo J.	Police Inspector	56	Civil Servant
	Rigoberto Valazquez	Junta President	26	Farmer
Cuchilla	Campos Elias B.	Police Inspector	38	Civil Servant
	Eduardo Buitrago	Junta President	45	Farmer
Cumbarco	Sr. Rincon	Police Inspector	?	Civil Servant
	Sr. Lopez	Junta President	?	Farmer
Palomino	Nostor Valencia L.	Police Inspector	41	Civil Servant
	Faustino Carmona O.	Junta President	50	Farmer
San Antonio	Bernardo Arias G.	Police Inspector	36	Civil Servant
	Alonso Arias A.	Junta President	28	Businessman
Venado	Omar Flores	Police Inspector	22	Civil Servant
	Serafin Sanchez	Junta President	29	Farmer
Caicedonia	Daniel Garcia L.	Mayor	32	Army Captain
	Miguel Suarez A.	Council President	?	Businessman
Aures	Jorge Melendez F.	Military Inspector	33	Army Lieut.
	Vicente Lopez	Junta President	45	Farmer
Crucero	Arturo Osorio	Police Inspector	55	Civil Servant
	Raul Sanchez Arias	Junta President	37	Farmer
Montegrande	Eduardo Peno E.	Police Inspector	22	Civil Servant
	Santiago Cortez	Junta President	32	Farmer
Samaria	Jose Arbelaez L.	Police Inspector	45	Civil Servant
	Alfonso Hoyos B.	Junta President	40	Farmer
Manzanillo	Ecuardo Rua	Junta President	52	Farmer
	Clementi Arenas	Junta President	60	Farmer

Source: Community Survey.

51

In addition to the public means of communication,
CVC and the Colombian Army operated private radios.

Of the eight corregimientos in Sevilla where
the cooperative would distribute electricity, none
had a postal service. Two of the villages, Palomino
and Venada, had telephone service. All of the villages had radio and television reception and that
was the extent of their communication facilities.

Caicedonia had postal service and was installing an automatic telephone system. Radio and television reception was good. None of the four corregimientos in the cooperative area had any means
of public communication. Aures and Samaria, however,
could use the army radio system for emergencies.

Employment and Wages

The city of Sevilla was the largest industrial
center in both municipios. Industry in Caicedonia
was concentrated primarily in the production of
panela. This also was the only industry in the
rural areas of either municipio.

Sevilla had several mechanic shops, a millin-
ery, a soap factory, a shirt factory, a candle factory, two coffee packaging plants, several leather
and furniture shops, five bakeries, two laundries,
four coffee grinding plants, two dairies, a slaugh-
ter house, two printing shops, a tile plant and
factories for making cigarettes, bricks and concrete tile.

Employment in the rural areas of Sevilla was
almost entirely in agriculture. The only people
gaining a livelihood outside agriculture in the
rural areas were those who were operating small general stores. The estimated number of workers,
stores and employees in the rural communities is
shown in Table 10.

Among the 12 rural villages surveyed there was
an estimated working force of 1,022. San Antonio

with more than three times as many workers as any
other village was the only community where the working force included women--estimated to be 25 women
earning an income outside the home. Corozal had
more stores than San Antonio, but it was located on
the railroad and at the edge of the coffee country
and the beginning of the grazing land.

Industry in Caicedonia included production of
panela, plants for producing bricks and tile, various commercial stores and small general stores.
The estimated employment in the city of Caicedonia
was 1,209.

TABLE 10

Total Number of Workers, Stores and
Employees in Rural Villages in the
Cooperative Area, March, 1965

Village	Total No. of Workers	No. of Stores	No. of Employees
Sevilla:			
Coloradas	80	3	3
Corozal	70	16	17
Cuchilla	30	3	3
Cumbarco	60	5	6
Manzanillo	50	1	2
Palomino	56	4	4
San Antonio	325	15	22
Venado	90	2	4
Caicedonia:			
Aures	75	2	2
Crucero	40	3	3
Montegrande	60	8	8
Samaria	86	6	12
Total:	1,022	68	86

Source: Community Survey.

According to most persons interviewed in the
rural areas, there was very little or no unemployment. Local sources said that when there was a
slack season in one area the workers would go to
another to seek employment. This was possible in
the project area because the variation in altitude
and the consequent variation in temperature permitted coffee to mature the year round. Thus, there
was almost always some coffee being harvested some-
where in both municipios.

Local sources also said that most workers
worked ten hours a day and five and a half days a
week. In some cases they said the workers worked
all seven days. In San Antonio, the Police Inspector said that approximately 50 workers or 17 percent of the labor force were not employed. In Palomino, 59 percent of the labor force was said to be
unemployed. In Caicedonia it was estimated that 32
percent of the workers were unemployed. Obviously,
unemployment meant different things to different
people and it was very difficult to obtain meaning-
ful information. No one seemed to have the concept
of underemployment. The majority of people seemed
to think that there was work for everyone all the
time.

From the discussions and observations during
the survey, it appeared that roughly 33 percent of
the male working force was unemployed most of the
time. The amount of disguised unemployment was
quite high and would be difficult to estimate. But
it was apparent that the same amount of production
could be achieved with considerably fewer number of
workers.

Periods of unemployment varied among the 12
rural communities. While there were periods of unemployment in the particular area, local sources
said the workers either went to other areas to work
or remained in the area to clean weeds and under-
growth from the crops. These were the periods when
there was no coffee being harvested. All communities, except Corozal and Montegrande, produce coffee
as the primary crop. Employment in these areas,

therefore, depended upon coffee harvesting. In
Montegrande sugar cane provided year round employment; in Corozal, it was livestock. The coffee harvesting months in the communities surveyed are
shown in Table 11.

Coffee harvesting wages were fairly consistent
throughout the area. Ten pesos with meals for a
ten-hour day was common practice. Daily wages without meals ranged from Col $14 to Col $18. On a contract basis, Col $10 to Col $12 per arroba was the
usual payment.* For the 12 communities, coffee harvesting wages are shown in Table 12. Wages for
other types of work are shown in Table 13.

TABLE 11

Months of Coffee Harvesting in Rural
Communities in Cooperative Area

Community	Months of Coffee Harvesting
Sevilla:	
Coloradas	March, April, May, Sept., Oct., Nov.
Corozal	April, May, Oct., Nov.
Cuchilla	March, April, May, Sept., Oct., Nov.
Cumbarco	May, June, July, Nov., Dec., Jan.
Manzanillo	March, April, May, Oct., Nov., Dec.
Palomino	April, May, June, Oct., Nov., Dec.
San Antonio	May, June, July, Oct., Nov., Dec.
Venado	April, May, June, Sept., Oct., Nov.
Caicedonia:	
Aures	May, June, July, Nov., Dec., Jan.
Crucero	June, July, Aug., Jan., Feb., March
Montegrande	March, April, May, Oct., Nov., Dec.
Samaria	April, May, June, Oct., Nov., Dec.

Source: Community Survey.

_____

*One arroba equals 25 pounds.

TABLE 12

Wages in Rural Communities for
Harvesting Coffee, March, 1965
(in pesos)

Community	Per Day with Meal	Per Day without Meal	Per Arroba without meal
Sevilla:			
Coloradas	10	15	--
Corozal	--	--	10
Cuchilla	--	15	--
Cumbarco	10	--	--
Manzanillo	--	15	--
Palomino	--	18	--
San Antonio	10	15	--
Venado	10	16	--
Caicedonia:			
Aures	10	14	10
Crucero	10	16	--
Montegrande	--	--	12
Samaria	12	--	12

Source: Community Survey.

TABLE 13

Wages According to Type of Work, March, 1965
(in pesos)

Type of Work	Daily with Meals	Daily without Meals
Platano	10	15
Cleaning	10	15
Fertilizing	10	15
Dairy	12 (all year)	--
Sugar cane	9 (all year)	12
Cacao	9	12
Beef cattle	11 (all year)	--

Source: Community Survey.

According to a SENA study, it takes 1,448 man-hours to produce 1 hectare of sugar cane for panela in the project area. To produce 1 hectare of corn, it takes 376 man-hours, for yuca 77 and for platano, 80 (see Table 14).

TABLE 14

Man-days Required to Produce One Hectare
of Sugar Cane and Corn According
to Type of Work

Type of Work	Sugar Cane (Man-days)*	Corn (Man-days)
Clearing the land	10	--
Preparing the land	12	12
Plowing	10	--
Seeding	10	2
Weeding	34	16
Harvesting	45	5
Transporting	15	2
Making panela	30	--
Transporting	5	--
Shelling	--	5
Administering	10	5
Total:	181	47

*One man-day equals eight hours of work by one man.

Source: SENA, Bogota.

Production and Production Methods

Because of the favorable soil and climate conditions, the base of the economy in the project area is coffee. Both municipios are covered by firm volcanic soils.

In some parts of the project area, the volcanic soil is more than a meter in thickness. Water is plentiful and the soil is well aerated. The soils are black and chocolate in color with an abundant amount of humus. They are rich in organic matter and can be prepared easily for planting. Water and air can penetrate the soil easily. Erosion of the soil is very slow, but there are areas in the municipios where it is noticeable and is obviously washing away part of the topsoil.

Coffee, corn, sugar cane, platano and yuca are the most important crops grown in the project area. Livestock and livestock products are also important in some areas. Coffee, sugar cane, beef and cacao are by far the most important commercial products. Corn, platano and yuca are the most important food crops. In addition, milk, pork and several types of fruits and vegetables are produced for local consumption.

Bananas and platano, which serve as shade for the coffee trees, are grown extensively throughout the area. Shade trees, such as the guamo, still serve as shade for coffee in many areas but platano is more common.

Coffee, platano, bananas, corn, yuca, cacao and fruit trees are often intercropped. Land dedicated to the cultivation of one crop is relatively scarce.

For each of the 12 communities surveyed, principal commercial crops and principal food crops are shown in Tables 15 and 16. The number of farms and the area in hectares in annual crop production in Sevilla and Caicedonia in 1958 are shown in Table 17.

TABLE 15

Principal Commercial Crops According
to Communities Surveyed, 1965

Community	Crops
Sevilla:	
Coloradas	Coffee, platano, yuca, beans
Corozal	Coffee, beef
Cuchilla	Coffee, platano, bananas
Cumbarco	Coffee, platano, corn, yuca
Manzanillo	Coffee, platano, yuca, beans
Palomino	Coffee
San Antonio	Coffee, platano, yuca, arracacha*
Venado	Coffee, platano, yuca, beans
Caicedonia:	
Aures	Coffee, platano, milk
Crucero	Coffee, platano
Montegrande	Coffee, panela, cacao, milk
Samaria	Coffee

*A root crop

Source: Community Survey.

TABLE 16

Principal Food Crops According to
Communities Surveyed, 1965

Community	Crops
Sevilla:	
Coloradas	Platano, yuca, arracacha, corn
Corozal	Platano, yuca, corn
Cuchilla	Platano, yuca, corn, arracacha
Cumbarco	Platano, yuca, corn
Manzanillo	Platano, yuca, oranges, beans
Palomino	Platano, yuca, oranges
San Antonio	Platano, yuca, arracacha, corn
Venado	Platano, yuca, corn, beans
Caicedonia:	
Aures	Platano, yuca, corn, arracacha
Crucero	Platano, yuca, corn, beans
Montegrande	Platano, yuca, milk, corn
Samaria	Platano, yuca, corn

Source: Community Survey.

TABLE 17

Number of Farms and Farm Area in Annual and Perennial Crops in Sevilla and Caicedonia, 1958

Crop	Sevilla		Caicedonia	
	No. of Farms	Total Hectares	No. of Farms	Total Hectares
Annual Crops:				
Cotton	1	.6	--	--
Barley	2	2.1	--	--
Beans	227	396.4	188	253.4
Corn	384	591.7	273	417.5
Potatoes	5	6.0	1	1.0
Pasto de corte*	10	10.0	9	4.9
Soybeans	1	.6	--	--
Tobacco	3	3.4	--	--
Wheat	7	35.2	--	--
Yuca	212	156.8	213	207.1
Total:	852	1,202.8	684	883.9
Perennial Crops:				
Bananas	117	52.7	2	1.9
Cacao	14	21.8	83	104.3
Coffee	1,745	10,956.4	891	6,597.6
Sugar cane	117	124.6	61	841.6
Lemons	468	--	246	--
Oranges	641	2.0	336	--
Platano	1,555	1,564.9	823	1,365.0
Pineapple	166	2.8	17	10.2
Grapes	2	1.9	--	--
Total:	4,825	12,727.1	2,459	8,920.6

*Grass cuttings used as fodder.

Source: SENA, Bogota.

   The Cooperativa de Caficultores de Caicedonia
estimated coffee production for the Municipio of
Caicedonia in 1963 at 25 million pounds. Table 18
shows the 1963 production of major crops in Caicedonia; average yield per hectare for the various
crops is shown in Table 19; Table 20 gives livestock
population in both municipios in 1958.

TABLE 18

Production of Major Crops in Caicedonia, 1963

Crop	Unit	Amount
Coffee	Arroba	1,000,000
Panela	Arroba	400,000
Cacao	Arroba	2,500
Platano	Carga	500,000
Tobacco	Kilo	2,880

   Source: Cooperativa de Caficultores de
Caicedonia.

TABLE 19

Yield per Hectare for Various Crops
in Caicedonia, 1963

Crop	Unit	Yield per Hectare
Coffee, parchment	Arroba	50
Coffee, cherry	Arroba	150
Corn	Kilo	2,000
Beans	Kilo	800
Yuca	Carga	45

   Source: Cooperativa de Caficultores de
Caicedonia.

TABLE 20

Livestock Population in Sevilla
and Caicedonia, 1958

Type of Livestock	Sevilla		Caicedonia	
	No. of Farms	No. of Head	No. of Farms	No. of Head
Cattle	427	18,988	312	7,450
Horses	782	1,529	386	729
Mules	264	611	231	712
Donkeys	24	28	5	9
Hogs	675	1,847	434	1,302
Sheep	12	148	5	20
Goats	5	26	3	28
Chickens	1,556	28,565	720	15,100
Other poultry	506	2,976	218	1,703

Source: Universidad del Valle, Cali.

Coffee production in Sevilla in 1963 according
to records of the Cooperativa de Caficultores de
Sevilla amounted to 1.4 million arrobas. This was
produced on 30,700 hectares by 3,000 coffee growers.
Data on the amount of land devoted to the production
of different crops in the Municipio of Sevilla are
given in the section on land use (see p. 67).

Coffee growers generally fertilize the soil
every six months. They use the pulp from the coffee
bean to add organic matter to the soil. Before
placing it on the land, the pulp is allowed to fer-
ment. Several farmers also use a chemical fertilizer sold through the Cooperativa de Caficultores.

The commercial fertilizer is used for the coffee
trees that are in production. Rate of application
varies widely but is usually around three <u>bultos</u>
per <u>plaza</u>* (285 pounds per acre). The fertilizer is
applied to both platano and coffee. Insecticides
are also used on the coffee trees. A dust-type insecticide is more common, although a liquid is also
used. In one case the insecticide was used in a
campaign to kill ants.

The commercial fertilizer weighed 100 pounds
per sack and five sacks were applied to each hectare. Each sack cost Col $65.00. Application in
Manzanillo was usually in June and December.

In Palomino, urea was applied to coffee at the
rate of from 1 to 4 bultos per plaza per year. Coffee growers in Venado used about 1/4 bulto per plaza
per year. In Caicedonia the coffee cooperative recommended 14-14-14, 12-12-17 and other types at the
rate of 250 grams per tree. Urea was recommended
for corn at the rate of 3 or 4 bultos per hectare
and to sugar cane at the same rate. It was apparent,
however, that in many cases commercial fertilizers
were not used and when they were used, the rate of
application was much less than that recommended by
the coffee cooperative.

Topography of the area will prevent any large-
scale mechanization of agriculture. In addition,
coffee, which is the predominant crop, depends to a
great extent upon manual labor. Harvesting of coffee at this time does not lend itself to mechanization. Only the cultivation of sugar cane, corn,
yuca and beans permits an extensive use of agricultural machinery.

Marketing Methods and Prices

The only means small farmers had for getting
their products to market were to carry the products

----

*1 bulto equals 150 pounds.
 1 plaza equals 1.6 acres.

on horseback or to hire jeeps. Sevilla and Caicedonia were the major marketing centers and transportation costs varied with the distance of the
farm from the market. Transportation costs for the
12 communities are shown in Table 21.

From Samaria it cost Col $2.00 for transporta-
tion to market of 1 arroba of cheese. It cost Col
$1.50 to transport 1 stalk of platano 14 kilometers,
and Col $20.00 to transport one pig to the market.

Marketing costs probably took a larger share
of the profit from platano than from any other
product. Prices at the market for most farmers
were from Col $4.00 to Col $7.00 per racimo (stalk)
and marketing costs ranged from Col $.50 to Col
$1.50 per racimo. Consequently, several farmers
sold their products at the farm to the jeep drivers
who would then market the products in Sevilla or
Caicedonia or possibly transport the products to
Armenia, Cali or another large city. Generally,
one jeep could transport 30 large racimos of platano
or 80 small racimos. Prices of various products on
sale at the local market in Sevilla at the time of
the survey are shown in Table 22.

Land Use, Farm Size and Ownership

Present land tenure has resulted primarily from
strong population pressure. People were attracted
to the land that was rich in fertility at one time
but now has been exploited. This movement left an
excessive balance of people to land area and today
most of the farms are small.

The number of farms with 1 hectare of land and
over and the amount of land in these farms in
Sevilla and Caicedonia in 1959 are shown in Table 23.

When asked the sizes of the smallest, largest
and most typical farms in the communities near the
villages, those responding gave the sizes of farms
in plazas as shown in Table 24.

TABLE 21

Transportation Costs in the
Cooperative Area, 1965

Community	Distance from Market (Kilometers)	Cost per Person (Col $)	Cost per Bulto (Col $)
Sevilla:			
Coloradas	9	2.50	2.50
Corozal	26	4.00	5.00*
Cuchilla	15	3.00	3.00
Manzanillo	10	2.50	2.50
Palomino	8	3.00	3.00
San Antonio	10	2.50	2.50
Venado	8	3.00	3.00
Caicedonia:			
Aures	25	4.00	3.00
Crucero	5	2.00	1.50
Montegrande	10	2.00	1.00
Samaria	14	3.00	1.00

*Corozal was the only village located on a rail-road line. Because of the mountainous terrain, it was considerably less expensive for the people to travel by train to Armenia or Zarzal even though it was a longer distance. It cost Col $5.00 to transport one bulto of coffee to Armenia, which was 35 kilometers away. It cost Col $4.00 to transport one can of milk (35 liters) to Sevilla by jeep. A person could ride to Sevilla by jeep for Col $1.00 or he could go by rail to Armenia much more comfortably and less expensively. The cost for one person by rail to Armenia was Col $.90. Zarzal was only 17 kilometers from Corozal and the cost by rail was Col $.80.

Source: Community Survey.

TABLE 22

Market Prices for Various Products
at Sevilla, 1965

Product	Unit	Price (Col $)
Coffee	Arroba	73.50
Yuca	Bulto	50.00
Arracacha	Bulto	65.00
Platano	Racimo	7.00
Beans	Pound	2.00
Beans	Arroba	60.00
Cheese	Arroba	100.00
Butter	Pound	8.50
Eggs	Each	.60
Oranges	Bulto	25.00
Corn	Bulto	75.00
Panela	Arroba	24.00
Panela	Atado*	2.00
Potatoes	Arroba	6.50
Alverja	Arroba	45.00
Milk	Bottle	1.10
Chocolate	Pound	6.50
Cacao	Arroba	73.50
Beef	Pound	4.50
Pork	Pound	7.00

*2 pieces of panela.

Source: Community Survey.

TABLE 23

Size of Farms in Sevilla and Caicedonia, 1959

Size of Farm (in hectares)	No. of Farms	% of Farms	Area in Hectares	% of Area
Sevilla:				
1-4.9	564	34	1,531.3	4
5-19.9	763	46	7,929.6	20
20-99.9	262	16	9,699.6	24
100-and over	75	4	21,213.2	52
Total:	1,664	100	40,373.7	100
Caicedonia:				
1-4.9	204	25	604.6	4
5-19.9	420	53	4,512.1	27
20-99.9	152	19	5,749.3	35
100-and over	23	3	5,660.8	34
Total:	799	100	16,526.8	100

Source: Community Survey.

TABLE 24

Size of Farms in the Cooperative Area, 1965
(in plazas)

Community	Smallest	Largest	Most Common
Sevilla:			
Coloradas	3	80	12
Corozal	5	1,000	300
Cuchilla	8	100	25
Cumbarco	10	1,000	100
Manzanillo	30	80	60
Palomino	3	50	25
San Antonio	10	100	50
Venado	8	1,000	30
Caicedonia:			
Aures	15	600	80
Crucero	7	200	35
Montegrande	1	1,100	30
Samaria	8	320	60

Source: Universidad del Valle, Cali.

The use of land and the number of hectares in both municipios in 1959 are shown in Table 25.

Land use in the 1959 census was further classified according to the type of farming as shown in Table 26.

According to the 1959 agricultural census, by far the majority of farms in Sevilla and Caicedonia were operated by farm owners. Those farms operated by administrators, however, were substantially larger than owner-operated farms. In some cases farm administrators were paid a salary and in other cases they received a percentage of the farm income.

According to information obtained during the survey, the percentage of farmers tilling their own soil and those having other arrangements were as shown in Table 27.

Income, Savings and Investment

Agricultural laborers made up the majority of the population in the small rural villages. Farm owners and store operators made up the remainder of the population. No attempt was made to determine the income of the store operators and the income of farm owners was obtained in the individual interviews. In this section, the financial situation of the agricultural laborers will be primarily discussed.

Generally, an agricultural laborer received Col $15 per day without meals, whether it was for harvesting coffee, working in platano or cleaning undergrowth from the farm. This was pay received for the actual number of days worked. On the average, according to local sources, the laborer worked 240 days a year. If he were fully employed he would receive an annual income of Col $3,600.

TABLE 25

Use of Land in Sevilla and Caicedonia, 1959
(in hectares)

Use of Land	Sevilla	Caicedonia
Arable land	1,634.9	658.5
Permanent crops	12,729.6	8,920.6
Grazing land	22,304.1	5,711.3
Mountains and woods	3,495.9	1,031.1
Other uses	729.0	248.5
Total:	40,893.5	16,578.0

Source: Universidad del Valle, Cali.

TABLE 26

Number of Farms and Hectares According to Type
of Farming in Sevilla and Caicedonia, 1959

Type of Farming	No. of Farms	No. of Hectares
Sevilla:		
Crop production	1,754	17,776.2
Dairy	31	2,795.8
Beef	103	8,114.6
Dairy and beef	25	4,279.7
Poultry	46	7.0
Mixed farming	38	5,384.5
Total:	1,997	38,357.8
Caicedonia:		
Crop production	883	11,497.0
Dairy	5	317.1
Beef	25	883.1
Dairy and beef	3	1,434.2
Poultry	1	.2
Mixed farming	30	2,376.0
Total:	947	16,507.6

Source: Universidad del Valle, Cali.

TABLE 27

Type of Farm Tenancy According to Percent
of Farms in Rural Communities, 1965
(in percent)

Community	Owner-Operated	Other Arrangements
Sevilla:		
Coloradas	80	20
Corozal	30	70
Cuchilla	90	10
Cumbarco	85	15
Manzanillo	50	50
Palomino	30	70
San Antonio	20	80
Venado	10	90
Caicedonia:		
Aures	10	90
Crucero	40	60
Montegrande	50	50
Samaria	20	80
Average:	43	57

Source: Community Survey.

Those laborers who had permanent year round
employment received slightly more income. They
were generally paid Col $10 per day with meals for
every day in the year. This gave them an annual
income of Col $3,650. Laborers working on dairy
farms received higher pay because of the longer
workday. Their income was Col $11 per day or Col
$4,015 annually with meals.

The majority of laborers, however, worked on
a daily basis. They were not always employed and
the annual income ranged from Col $2,000 to Col
$3,000. An estimate of income for all workers, per-
manent and temporary, was approximately Col $3,000.

Local sources said the village families were almost always in debt. Sometimes they would receive loans from the National Federation of Coffee Growers or from a local bank. Interest for these loans was about 12 percent. The most usual form of debt, however, was for purchases charged at a village store. There was no interest charged for these debts, but local sources said prices at the stores were sufficient to cover any interest that might be lost.

Debts at the stores were usually incurred during periods when coffee was not being harvested in the local area. When the workers were employed again, they would pay their debts to the store owner. Typical debts during periods of unemployment ranged as follows: Col $50 weekly, Col $80 to Col $280 monthly, or Col $1,200 for six months.

A very small percentage (16 percent) of the village families, including store and farm owners, had accounts in banks in Sevilla, Caicedonia or elsewhere (see Table 28).

There was practically no savings reported in any of the villages. The only persons with savings, according to local sources, were those with bank accounts. They estimated annual savings for these families to be from Col $100 to Col $360 per year. Investments, if any, were not known.

Energy and Fuel Availability

According to the 1959 agricultural census, human energy was the sole source of power on the majority of farms in Sevilla and Caicedonia. Only one farm in Sevilla used electric energy, while ten farms in Caicedonia either purchased electric power or produced it on the farms (see Table 29).

The city of Sevilla had been served for a number of years by a municipally owned hydroelectric plant with a capacity of 450 kilowatts. It also used a diesel generator with a capacity of 720 kilowatts. In 1963 CVC extended its transmission lines to Sevilla and the city supplemented locally

TABLE 28

Number of Families in Rural Villages with Bank Accounts, 1965

Community	No. of Families	No. of Bank Accounts	% of Families with Accounts
Sevilla:			
Coloradas	20	6	30
Corozal	70	5	7
Cuchilla	15	0	0
Cumbarco	30	5	17
Manzanillo	30	6	20
Palomino	16	3	19
San Antonio	100	10	10
Venado	30	4	13
Caicedonia:			
Aures	35	10	29
Crucero	30	7	23
Montegrande	20	10	50
Samaria	43	6	14
Total:	439	72	16

Source: Community Survey.

TABLE 29

Sources of Energy and Number of Farms in Sevilla and Caicedonia Using Energy, 1959

	No. of Farms	
Source of Energy	Sevilla	Caicedonia
Mechanical power	313	298
Animal and mechanical	1	1
Human energy	1,706	651
Electric energy:		
Purchased	1	4
Produced	--	6

Source: Universidad del Valle, Cali.

produced energy with power purchased from the CVC
grid system. At the time of the survey in March,
1965, Sevilla purchased power during the day from
CVC. In the evenings the CVC power would be turned
off and energy produced by the local generating system would be distributed.

The electric distribution system in Sevilla was
old. CVC estimated that 40 percent of the energy
was lost because of the antiquated distribution system. This meant that the city was paying for 40
percent more energy than it was consuming. Wires
were strung under rooftops and presented fire hazards in many areas. Wiring in the homes also needed
to be improved.

Of the reported fires in Sevilla in 1962, five
were caused from short circuits; in 1963, eight such
fires; and in 1964 ten such fires, two of them the
result of primary line failures.[10]

Caicedonia had a newly installed distribution
system and was receiving power from the transmission
line that had been extended from Sevilla to Caicedonia in 1964. Previously, Caicedonia had received
energy from two diesel generators located in Caicedonia that were operated by CVC.

Electrification on the farms surveyed showed a
marked increase in the use of electricity from 1959
when the agricultural census was conducted. In addition to several private generating plants on the
farms, several plants were being used in the villages (see Table 30). In some cases, the owner of
a private generating plant was selling energy to
his neighbors. The cost for this type of electricity in Corozal was Col $10 for one bulb per month.
In San Antonio the cost was Col $2.50 per month for
one bulb, Col $3.00 for a record player and Col
$2.00 for a radio.

Almost all of the private plants in the villages were used in stores. They were usually operated for three or four hours in the evenings and
in some cases all day Sunday.

TABLE 30

Number of Generating Plants and Use of
Electricity in Rural Villages in
Cooperative Area, 1965

Community	No. of Plants	Uses of Electricity
Sevilla:		
Coloradas	0	--
Corozal	6	Lights, radio, record player
Cuchilla	0	--
Cumbarco	2	Lights, radio
Manzanillo	2	Lights
Palomino	*	Lights and small appliances
San Antonio	2	Lights, radio, record player
Venado	2	Lights, radio, iron, record player
Caicedonia:		
Aures	1	Lights, dispulping coffee
Crucero	2	Lights, iron, refrigerator, radio, record player
Montegrande	1	Lights
Samaria	2	Lights, radio

*Palomino was located near the distribution
line extending from Sevilla. The village had received electricity for approximately 25 years.
Each consumer paid Col $100 for a meter and Col
$.22 for each kilowatt-hour.

Source: Community Survey.

Prices of fuels varied considerably throughout
the project area (see Table 31). Usually prices
were highest in those villages most distant from
Sevilla or Caicedonia. Gasoline and kerosene were
often sold in the small villages, but diesel fuel
and oil were only sold in Sevilla and Caicedonia.

TABLE 31

Prices of Fuel in Cooperative Area, 1965
(in pesos)

Community	Gasoline (Gallon)	Kerosene (Gallon)	Diesel (Gallon)	Oil (Quart)
Sevilla:				
Coloradas	1.55	1.80	1.80	6.30
Corozal	2.20	2.00	--	--
Cuchilla	1.60	2.00	--	6.00
Cumbarco	3.00	--	--	--
Manzanillo	2.00	--	--	--
Palomino	--	--	--	--
San Antonio	2.00	2.00	--	--
Venado	2.50	2.00	--	--
Caicedonia:	2.50	2.00	--	--
Aures	1.55	1.35	1.35	6.00
Crucero	--	--	--	--
Montegrande	2.20	2.00	--	--
Samaria	--	--	--	--
	2.00	1.80	--	--

Source: Community Survey.

75

DEVELOPMENT OF THE COOPERATIVE

The Se-Ca Rural Electric Cooperative Project was developed "to electrify a region of intensive farming of coffee, bananas, oranges, yuca and related products" in the Cauca Valley. It was to serve the "needs of its consumers through a self-help project." The towns were "to serve as a nucleus so that power lines could be extended to its supporting farm and trade areas."[11]

Initial Investigation

AID contracted with the National Rural Electric Cooperative Association (NRECA) on November 1, 1962, to "provide technical assistance for the development of rural electrification, rural industries and community facilities in the developing countries."[12]

That same month, Louis B. Strong, an NRECA rural electrification specialist, began an assignment in Colombia to conduct an initial investigation and organization of the cooperative area.

In his report Strong stated:

> The Sevilla and Caicedonia areas, with fairly large concentrations of potential users of electricity and with the consumers presently receiving electricity paying a fairly high rate for very poor service, would seem to provide a good location for a pilot rural electrification project.
> This project would provide a pattern for treating larger rural towns supported by agricultural production and the farms around that town as a single project with electric rates at a level sufficient to support electrification in both the towns and the farms of the area.

Strong concluded that rural farms in Colombia

could not be supplied as separate projects at rates comparable to that now
being paid by urban users. So it is
apparent that either:
   1. Farm users must pay consid-
       erably higher rates for
       electricity than city users.
   2. Some type of subsidy must be
       introduced into farm elec-
       trification.
   3. Town and farm users must be
       grouped together and given a
       composite rate.
   4. Or some combination of the
       above systems must be worked
       out.[13]

It was apparent that if farm users were to pay
higher rates for electricity than city users, rural
electrification would have to wait many years in
the Cauca Valley. Therefore, a combination of alternatives 2 and 3 were incorporated into the project.

Engineering Aspects

Design of the distribution system was based on
CVC standards and on specifications developed by
the Rural Electrification Administration (REA) in
the U.S. Department of Agriculture. The system as
designed was expected to be sufficient to meet demand for ten years after energization. It was assumed that any growth in demand in this period
could be supplied by construction financed by accumulated margins. Distribution lines to be constructed are shown in Map 3.

Electric power for the rural electric cooperative was to be supplied by CVC through its grid system, using thermo and hydro energy. Concrete poles
were to be used throughout the distribution system.
The pole construction plant used by CVC is mobile

MAP 3
LOCATION OF COOPERATIVE
DISTRIBUTION LINES

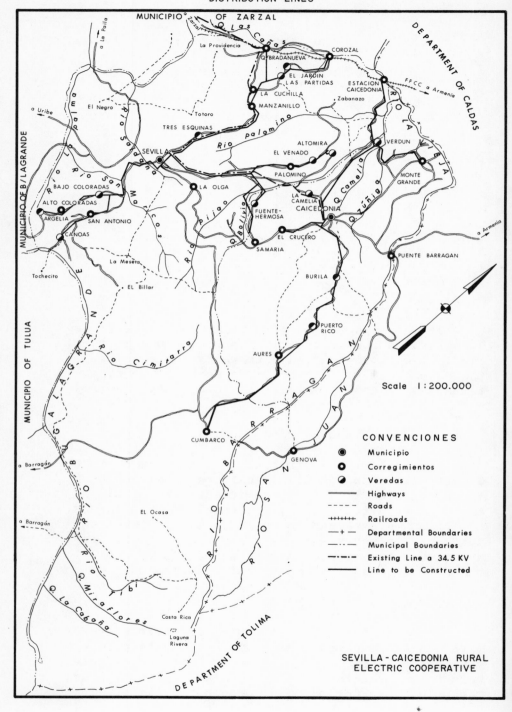

Scale 1:200.000

CONVENCIONES

◉ Municipio
◎ Corregimientos
◑ Veredas
── Highways
---- Roads
+++++ Railroads
─+─ Departmental Boundaries
─·─ Municipal Boundaries
─··─ Existing Line a 34.5 KV
━━ Line to be Constructed

SEVILLA - CAICEDONIA RURAL
ELECTRIC COOPERATIVE

and poles were to be constructed in the project
area. Crossarms were to be obtained locally and
constructed of camino wood. This wood is considered to be of excellent quality and has been used
for many years. All transformers were to be single
phase.

Following is a description of engineering aspects described in the loan application:

Transmission--
     Existing: 7.5 miles 34.5 KV #4/0
                 13.6 miles 34.5 KV #2/0
     Under Construction: 3.3 miles 34.5 KV #2

     Transmission line built basically single pole
     type construction, concrete poles, wood cross-
     arms, designed to light leading (U.S. National
     Electric Safety Code [NESC]) standards.

Distribution--
     Primary line:
        26 miles 7.6/13.2 KV three-phase #1/0 Copper
        12.8 miles 7.6/13.2 KV three-phase #2 6/1
            ACSR (Aluminum Cable Steel Reinforced)

        4 miles 7.6/13.2 KV V-phase #1/0 ACSR
        3 miles 7.6/13.2 KV V-phase #2 6/1 ACSR

        1.0 mile 7.6 KV Single-phase #1/0 Copper
        21.7 mile 7.6 KV Single-phase #2 6/1 ACSR
        118.6 mile 7.6 KV Single-phase #4 7/1 ACSR

        187.1 total primary miles.

     Secondary and Service:
        15.3 miles 3W Underbuild #4 7/1 ACSR
        1.1 miles 2W Underbuild #4 7/1 ACSR
        5.21 miles 3W Services
        16.2 miles 2W Services

        38.03 Total Secondary and Service.

Primary Conductor--1/0 Copper, #2 6/1 ACSR, #4 7/1 ACSR.

Poles--Reinforced concrete.

Crossarms--Camino wood.

Transformers--Conventional.

Protective Equipment--Oil circuit breakers, reclosers, fuses and lightning arresters.

System Capacity--Not to exceed 6-volt drop at an average usage of 155 KWH/month/consumer after 10 years load growth.

Type System--Village/urban distribution and radial lines into rural areas.

Construction Standards--Design standards comparable to those of the REA. Strength and clearance specifications will be in accordance to NESC.

Substations--Quebradaneuva (new) 300 KVA 34.5/ 13.2 KV.

Power Supplier--Corporacion Autonoma Regional Del Cauca (CVC).

Delivery Point--Metering point located approximately 8.7 miles east of Zarsal substation.

Supply Characteristics--Maximum voltage 34.5 KV minimum voltage 32.0 KV, nominal voltage 33.0 KV.

90% Power Factor, 60 cycle.

Source of Supply--Zarsal substation of 20,000 KVA capacity, 115/34.5 KV. The 115 KV transmission line is a part of the CVC system and connects to the generation at Yumbo and at Calima No. 1.

Financial Aspects

The total cost of the project was estimated at approximately $1.3 million. On May 11, 1964, AID approved the loan request for $1 million. The remainder was to be provided by CVC.

Detailed costs of the project are shown in Table 32. Of the estimated total cost of $1,222,341 for the system, it was estimated that $681,654 or Col $9,202,325 would be required to build the distribution lines outside the cities of Sevilla and Caicedonia. The total estimated rural construction costs were broken down as shown in Table 33.

Retail rate schedules were to provide a minimum monthly bill of Col $5.00 to each consumer (see Table 34). It was anticipated at the time of the loan application that the wholesale rate charged to the cooperative by CVC would be Col $.8 or 8 centavos per KWH. At the time of the survey in March, 1965, however, it was anticipated that the wholesale rate would be Col $.125 per KWH.

The $1-million loan for construction of the Se-Ca Rural Electric Cooperative had to be processed by two other organizations before reaching the cooperative. AID made the loan to the Colombian Power Development Institute (Instituto de Aprovechamiento de Aguas y Fomento Electrico--Electraguas). Electraguas, as the borrower acting for the Colombian Government was to loan the funds to the regional power authority, CVC. The CVC in turn was to loan the funds to the cooperative.

Loan funds were made available to the borrower at an interest rate of 2 percent per annum repayable over 35 years. The first interest payment is due 6 months after the first disbursement. The first principal payment is due 9.5 years after the first interest payment. The loan is to be repaid in 51 semiannual installments.

TABLE 32

Detailed Costs of the Se-Ca Rural Electric
Cooperative, Estimated 1963
(in dollars)

Item	Total Cost
Transmission:	
7.5 miles 34.5 KV #4/0	36,000
13.6 miles 34.5 KV #2/0	40,000
3.3 miles 34.5 KV #2	16,000
Subtotal	92,000
Substations:	
Sevilla Substation	
4,000 KVA 34.5/13.2 KV	39,073
Caicedonia Substation	
1,500 KVA 34.5/13.2 KV	16,000
Quebradaneuva Substation	
300 KVA 34.5/13.2 KV	12,500
Subtotal	67,573
Distribution:	
Caicedonia distribution	75,000
Sevilla distribution	171,550
Rural distribution:	
Substation No. 1 Area	54,410
Substation No. 2 Area	177,955
Substation No. 3 Area	157,652
Subtotal	636,567
General plant equipment, tools and working equipment	36,000
Operating fund for 1st year of operation	60,000
Funds to relend for wiring & appliances	25,000
Contingency and inflation (17% local currency, 10% foreign exchange)	185,801
Inventory and engineering	78,400
Technical services	41,000
Total:	1,222,341

Source: Loan Application.

TABLE 33

Cost of Rural Portion of Total Construction Costs, Estimated 1965

Item	U.S. Dollars	Colombian Pesos*
Transmission	46,000	621,000
Substations	40,367	540,495
Distribution	390,017	5,265,230
General plant equipment	18,000	243,000
Operating fund	30,000	405,000
Funds to relend	5,000	67,500
Contingency and inflation	92,900	1,254,150
Inventory and engineering	39,200	529,200
Technical services	20,500	276,750
	681,654	9,202,325

*Converted at the official exchange rate of 13.5 to 1.

Source: Based on data contained in Loan Application.

TABLE 34

Retail Rates According to Schedule of Uses, 1963 (in pesos)

		Kilowatt-Hours/Consumer/Month		
	Schedule	0-20 KWH*	21-100 KWH	Over 100 KWH
A	City residential	5.00	.24	.23
B	City commercial	6.00	.25	.24
R	Rural residential	6.00	.26	.24
C	Rural commercial	6.50	.26	.24

*Minimum monthly bill for 20 KWH or less.

Source: Loan Application.

Electraguas as the borrower is to loan the funds to CVC at an interest rate not to exceed 2 percent and for a duration of not less than 35 years. The grace period is not to exceed 10 years. CVC then is to loan the funds to the cooperative at an interest rate not to exceed 2 percent for a duration of not less than 35 years. The grace period is not to exceed 5 years. Projection of the financial status of the cooperative according to the year of operation is shown in Table 35.

Organization

The Se-Ca Rural Electric Cooperative was legally recognized as the Cooperativa Integral de Electrificacion Sevilla-Caicedonia on December 11, 1964.

Some opposition to organization of the cooperative caused delay in meeting the conditions precedent to initial financing. The delay in disbursement of funds consequently caused a delay in construction of the distribution system.

In addition to organizing a new cooperative organization it was necessary to dissolve the existing organizations supplying electric energy in the towns of Sevilla and Caicedonia. There was little opposition in Caicedonia even though the town had a new distribution system and was receiving power from CVC's grid system. CVC owned 60 percent of the shares of the Caicedonia system, the Department of Valle 20 percent and the Municipio of Caicedonia 20 percent. The decision to dissolve the Caicedonia system became unanimous and the cooperative was free to operate in the Municipio of Caicedonia.

Even though Sevilla had an antiquated distribution system with electric lines strung under the edges of roofs and was losing an estimated 40 percent of energy, there was a great deal of opposition to dissolving the Sevilla system. The Junta was divided in its decision to turn the system over to the cooperative for a complete rebuilding.

TABLE 35

Financial Projection for Se-Ca Project, 1963

(in dollars)

Item	Years		
	1	5	10
Cash Flow Statement			
Source of funds:			
Net income for operations	47,266	100,227	163,078
Depreciation	12,358	11,400	10,325
Borrowing (AID)	1,004,384	--	--
Initial contribution (CVC)	218,000	--	--
Total source of funds	1,282,008	111,627	173,403
Application of funds:			
Construction	1,060,384	--	--
Consultant	41,000	--	--
Current assets	91,000	--	--
Debt service:			
Amortization (AID)	--	--	33,500
Amortization (CVC)	--	--	7,266
Interest (AID)	10,000	20,088	17,408
Interest (CVC)	--	4,360	3,780
Total debt service	10,000	24,448	61,954
Other expenditures	30,000	--	--
Total application of funds	1,232,384	24,448	61,954
Net cash accrual	49,624	97,179	101,124

(Continued)

85

TABLE 35 (Continued)

Item	Years		
	1	5	10
Income Statement			
Revenues from operations:			
Total revenues	207,099	298,445	405,613
Cost of operations:			
Operating expense	137,475	176,412	221,294
Fixed charges	22,358	21,806	21,261
Total cost	159,833	198,218	242,555
Profit and loss:			
Net income from operation	47,266	100,227	163,078
Less interest (AID)	11,480	11,480	11,480
Net profit	35,786	88,747	151,598
Less interest (CVC)	2,491	2,491	2,491
Profit and loss	33,295	86,256	149,107

Source: Loan Application with adjustments for actual interest payments.

86

There had been little opposition to formation
of the electric cooperative and it was anticipated
that the City Council would readily permit the cooperative to build a new distribution system. But
those concerned with development of the cooperative
had overlooked the power of politics.

Feasibility of the project that would serve
9,000 consumers was based on including the city of
Sevilla in the cooperative. It was imperative that
the Municipal Council approve by formal vote the replacement of the existing municipal system by the
cooperative system. Under Colombian procedures,
the 16-member council would need to vote three
times on the issue.

On the first vote in November, 1964, the council voted 8 to 0 in favor of the cooperative. This
opened the issue for debate. It soon became apparent that the three council members of the political
party representing the extreme left were opposed to
the cooperative. Two council members of the extreme
right also fell in line and the combined strength of
the extremists was five.

There was a great deal of campaigning by the
opposition. One of the five council members opposed
to the cooperative owned a radio station; another
edited a newspaper. In addition to radio and newspaper campaigning, the opposition handed out leaf-
lets to oppose the cooperative. But they gained
little support.

On the second vote the council voted 8 to 5 in
favor of the cooperative. This was thought to be
the critical vote. It was understood that party
headquarters in Bogota had sent word to the extremists not to oppose the cooperative any longer. But
if there was such a message, the council members
did not heed its instructions. Their opposition
became more intensified.

In order for the cooperative to win support on
the third vote there had to be a two-thirds approval

of the 16 council members. This meant that if the
five in opposition could convince one more member,
they could block the cooperative. And operation of
the entire cooperative depended on its approval in
Sevilla.

In addition to political philosophy, two of
the five members had personal reasons to be concerned. The council member owning the radio station
was paying Col $40 a month (approximately $3 at the
official exchange rate) for all the electricity he
needed to operate the station. The cooperative
would provide meters and consumers would pay according to the amount of electricity used. Undoubtedly,
it would cost more than Col $40 a month for elec-
tricity to operate a radio station.

The father of the editor of the newspaper operated a bakery. He also was paying about Col $40 a
month for electricity. Local sources said the newspaper did not pay for itself and the bakery was the
main source of income for the family. It is unknown
whether or not this was true, but it is known that
the electric bill would increase if metered.

Twice the council met to vote on the issue for
the third time, but the opposition managed to fili-
buster and prevent a vote. At another meeting, not
all of those in favor of the cooperative were present. Farmers from the surrounding areas traveled
over the mountainous roads repeatedly in order to
attend the meetings and show support for the cooperative. It was estimated that about 150 farmers attended each of these meetings. They showed their
support by chanting "Queremos luz!" "We want
lights!"

The third vote was called for March 8. All
members of the council approving the cooperative
were able to attend the meeting. Those opposed
realized they were defeated and did not attend.
Thus, the cooperative issue passed by the required
two-thirds approval. Final vote was 11 to 0 in
favor of the cooperative building a new distribution system in Sevilla.

Membership

Each member of the Se-Ca Rural Electric Cooperative was to be charged a fee of Col $155 for shares and membership. In March, 1965, at the time of the field survey, there were approximately 400 potential consumers who already had paid their membership fees. Projected membership of the cooperative within three years after energization is shown in Table 36. The estimated number of rural consumers within three years after the cooperative became energized is shown in Table 37.

TABLE 36

Projected Membership of the Cooperative within Three Years after Construction According to the Type of Consumer and Location, 1965

Type of Consumer	Substation #1	Substation #2	Substation #3	Substation #4
City:				
Residential	--	4,500	2,200	6,700
Commercial	--	400	200	600
Subtotal:	--	4,900	2,400	7,300
Rural:				
Residential	350	350	320	1,020
Commercial farms	100	350	230	680
Subtotal:	450	700	550	1,700
Total	450	5,600	2,950	9,000

Source: Estimates made during field survey.

TABLE 37

Estimated Rural Membership within Three Years after Construction, 1965

Community	Rural Residential	Commercial Farms	Type of Consumers
Substation No. 1:			
Quebradaneuva	200	25	225
La Cuchilla	15	5	20
Manzanillo	30	5	35
Corozal	70	25	95
Other	35	40	75
Subtotal:	350	100	450
Substation No. 2:			
Tres Esquinas	30	10	40
San Antonio	100	60	160
Coloradas	30	50	80
Crucero	30	20	50
Canoas	15	40	55
Samaria	45	30	75
Palomino	20	40	60
Venado	30	50	80
Other	50	50	100
Subtotal:	350	350	700
Substation No. 3:			
Montegrande	20	40	60
Aures	35	25	60
Cumbarco	30	50	80
Camelia	200	50	250
Other	35	65	100
Subtotal:	320	230	550
Total:	1,020	680	1,700

Source: Estimates made during field survey.

Construction

Construction of the distribution system was to
be handled by CVC as contractor to the cooperative.
CVC was to carry out construction on a straight
cost basis under supervision of a U.S. rural electrification specialist. CVC planned to build the
system in Sevilla and to subcontract work in the
rural area.

Lines were to be energized and all equipment
tested prior to the lines being turned over to the
cooperative. All equipment was to carry a one-year
free replacement guarantee.

Total construction time was estimated at nine
months. The general construction plan was:

1. Detail engineering and stake lines.
2. Draw plans and specifications.
3. Breakdown of construction units into items.
4. Assemble all material and make necessary
orders.
5. Start sign-up of members and easements.
6. Release staking sheets to start construction.
    a. Transport poles.
    b. Frame poles.
    c. Dig holes, set and tamp poles and set
anchors.
    d. String wire and install conductors.
    e. Hang transformers and run services.
    f. Set meters and energize.

Operation

The cooperative is privately owned. Its gov-
erning body consists of (1) the members' General
Assembly, (2) the Board of Directors and (3) the
Board of Control or Audit Board.

The General Assembly, composed of the entire
membership, is the highest authority. Direction
and administration of the cooperative is vested in
a Board of Directors. The board consists of six

members elected by the General Assembly, including
a president and secretary. Officers of the board
serve for one year while all board members serve
three-year terms.

The manager is appointed by the Board of Directors. He has the direct management of the operations of the cooperative under the supervision of
the Board of Directors. Manuel A. Criales, a CVC-
trained employee, was employed by the Se-Ca Board
of Directors as the first manager. For two years
previous to his appointment Criales had worked on
the organization of the cooperative. He was elected
provisional manager of the cooperative by the membership at the first general assembly in 1964. He
served in this capacity until being appointed manager by the Board of Directors. In 1964 Criales attended a 16-week course in the United States on
"Organization and Operation of Rural Electric Cooperatives."

The General Assembly also elects an Audit
Board, composed of a president, a secretary and a
General Assembly member. The functions of this
board include verification of audits and supervision
of the administrators.

Bylaws of the cooperative set forth in detail
the manner in which the cooperative is to be operated.

The main office of the rural electric cooperative is located in Sevilla with a branch office in
Caicedonia. Total personnel needed by the cooperative after energization was estimated at 29 as
shown in Table 38.

An agreement to establish an understanding of
supplemental assistance by CVC to the cooperative
was developed. The assistance was to be in the
form of operation, maintenance, billing, collecting,
accounting and engineering and technical service.
The agreement was to provide that as soon as the cooperative becomes financially able it will either

TABLE 38

Estimated Personnel of the Cooperative
after Construction, 1963

Position	Number
Manager	1
Superintendent or General Foreman	1
Cashiers	2
Meter readers	3
Electricians	8
Driver-helpers	6
Helpers	7
Watchmen	1
	29

Source: Loan Application.

pay CVC for these services or assume responsibility
for such service itself.

In accordance with the loan agreement, Electraguas contracted with the NRECA to provide a
rural electrification specialist to supervise and
advise on matters concerning the cooperative for a
period of at least one year after completion of
construction.

The Se-Ca Rural Electric Cooperative was energized on January 2, 1965, when the municipal system
in Caicedonia was dissolved. The cooperative assumed operations and the distribution system has
been operating in the name of the cooperative since
that time.

By October, 1965, the cooperative had approximately 2,000 members. About 50 percent of the

members had paid their full membership fee and the
remainder were paying the fee over the allowable
ten-month period. Total cost for each new member
was Col $155; the nonrefundable membership fee was
Col $5; and the cost of three shares was Col $150.

About half of the 1,963 electric consumers in
Caicedonia were members of the cooperative, while
Sevilla had about 800 members. Rural members numbered 160 in Caicedonia, 147 in Sevilla. None of
the rural members were receiving electricity.

In Sevilla there were 3,780 consumers receiving electricity from the antiquated distribution
system. Because of the long delay in building the
cooperative distribution system, those on the town
council opposed to the cooperative had attempted to
rescind the resolution permitting the cooperative
to operate in Sevilla. Their proposal to rescind
the resolution, however, was defeated on the second
vote in September, 1965.

Consumption of electricity in Caicedonia per
consumer was markedly higher than in Sevilla--about
90 KWH per month compared to 50 KWH.

PRE-ELECTRIFICATION SURVEY

The Consumer Survey was conducted in the cooperative area during February and March, 1965. Fifty
potential rural consumers of electric energy were
interviewed, 25 in each municipio.

Map 4 shows locations of the farms where interviews were conducted. Names of the respondents residing at the farms have been withheld to protect
their private affairs.

Separate interviews were conducted with six
rural schools in the two municipios. Schools interviewed are represented on the map by small letters.
Names of the schools and the nearest village were:
(1) La Magdalena, Canoas; (2) La Consolita, Samaria;

MAP 4
LOCATION OF INTERVIEWS
IN COOPERATIVE AREA

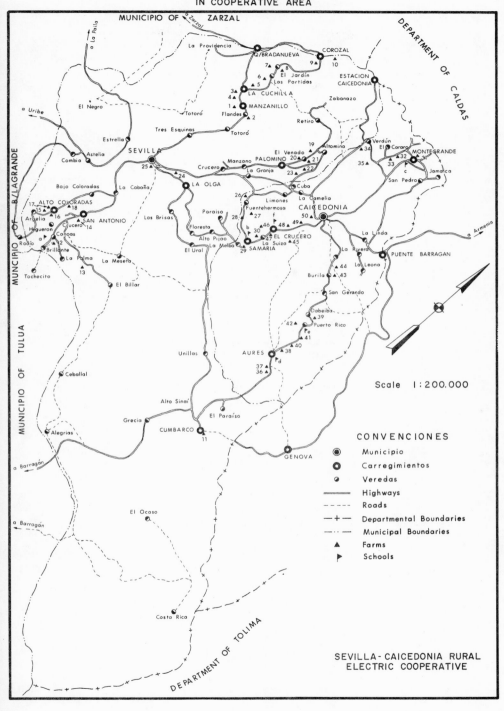

MUNICIPIO OF ZARZAL

DEPARTMENT OF CALDAS

MUNICIPIO OF B/LAGRANDE

MUNICIPIO OF TULUA

DEPARTMENT OF TOLIMA

La Providencia
Q/BRADANUEVA
COROZAL
7
8
9
10
El Jardín
6
Las Partidas
5
ESTACION
CAICEDONIA
3
LA CUCHILLA
4
Zabanazo
1
MANZANILLO
Flandes
2
Retiro
a La Paila
El Negro
Totoró
Totoró
Tres Esquinas
Estrella
Astelia
Combia
a Uribe
SEVILLA
25
24
Crucero
Manzano
PALOMINO
El Venado
19
20
21
Altomira
Verdún
34
El Cararo
MONTEGRANDE
33
32
35
La Granja
23
22
c
Jamaica
La Cabaña
LA OLGA
Cuba
San Pedro
Bajo Coloradas
26
La Camelia
17
ALTO COLORADAS
18
Limones
CAICEDONIA
15
16
Paraiso
Fuentehermosa
27
50
La Linda
SAN ANTONIO
Las Brisas
28
b
a Armenia
14
Argelia
Floresta
30
46
EL CRUCERO
Higueron
Alto Pijao
47
48
49
La Rivera
Canoas
La Melba
La Suiza
45
2
La Palma
El Ural
29
SAMARIA
La Leona
Rodio
Brillante
PUENTE BARRAGAN
13
La Meseta
44
a
La Mesera
Burila
43
Tochecito
El Billar
San Gerardo
Dabeiba
39
42
Puerto Rico
Pe
41
Unillas
AURES
40
38
d
37
36
Ceballal
Alto Sinaí
Grecia
El Paraiso
Alegrias
CUMBARCO
11
a Barragán
GENOVA
a Barragán
El Ocaso
Costa Rica

Scale 1:200.000

CONVENCIONES

◉	Municipio
◎	Carregimientos
◔	Veredas
———	Highways
- - - -	Roads
—+—	Departmental Boundaries
—·—	Municipal Boundaries
▲	Farms
▶	Schools

SEVILLA-CAICEDONIA RURAL
ELECTRIC COOPERATIVE

(3) San Isidro, Montegrande; (4) Nuestra Senora de
Fatima, Aures; (5) Puerto Rico; and (6) San Fran-
cisco, El Crucero.

Intended Uses of Electricity

The intended uses of electricity varied greatly among the 50 respondents (see Table 39). A few
farms were intending to use electricity only for
lights and one or two other appliances, while other
farms were intending to purchase several appliances
and utility motors. In some cases the appliances
and motors already had been purchased.

TABLE 39

Intended Uses of Electricity by 50 Farms in
the Cooperative Area within One Year after
the Availability of Electricity, 1965

Use	Sevilla	Caicedonia	Total
Incandescent bulbs (house)	194	394	588
Incandescent bulbs (other)	33	131	164
Fluorescent tubes	22	28	50
Infrared bulbs	12	14	26
Radio	23	27	50
Iron	26	29	55
Television	6	2	8
Refrigerator	11	6	17
Washing machine	5	2	7
Water pump	7	2	9
Incubator	1	--	1
Sewing machine	1	--	1
Utility motors:			
1/2 HP	4	--	4
1 HP	5	--	5
1 1/2 HP	7	2	9
2 HP	3	7	10
3 HP	2	4	6
5 HP	--	2	2
50 HP	--	2	2

Source: Consumer Survey.

Respondents were asked what use they intended to make of electricity during the first year that it became available. Then they were asked what other appliances they expected to purchase during the next two years. The results showed the uses of electricity for lighting and motors would increase slightly; purchase of radios, televisions, washing machines, refrigerators, pressure water systems and infrared bulbs would increase considerably more.

During the first year after electricity became available the respondents expected to purchase most of their lighting, irons, radios and utility motors. There was little difference in results of the survey between Sevilla and Caicedonia, except for lighting. Larger farms in Caicedonia, particularly one large coffee farm and two relatively large sugar cane farms, accounted for a substantially larger purchase of electric light bulbs in Caicedonia than in Sevilla.

Purchase of electric irons was expected to exceed those of radios during the first year. Total purchases of irons averaged more than one per farm, while the number of radios to be used during the first year averaged exactly one per consumer. Among those interviewed in Sevilla only one respondent said he would not purchase an electric iron during the first year nor within three years. He planned to use only two light bulbs and one small motor for dispulping coffee.

In Caicedonia three respondents said they did not intend to purchase electric irons during the first year nor within three years. One of the three intended to purchase a motor to dispulp coffee and the other two intended to purchase radios, but that was the extent to which they intended to use electricity. Thus, all but four respondents intended to purchase electric irons and they all intended to make their purchases during the first year.

Intended uses of electricity within three years after it became available are shown in Table 40.

Again, respondents in Caicedonia intended to use
twice as many electric light bulbs as the respondents in Sevilla. The number of radios and irons
to be used within three years was almost exactly
the same for the sample in Sevilla as it was for
the sample in Caicedonia. Respondents in Sevilla,
however, intended to use electricity to a greater
extent for television, refrigerators, washing machines and water pumps.

TABLE 40

Intended Uses of Electricity by 50 Farms
within Three Years after the Availability
of Electricity, 1965

Use	Sevilla	Caicedonia	Total
Incandescent bulbs (house)	237	470	707
Incandescent bulbs (other)	70	329	399
Fluorescent tubes	32	54	86
Infrared bulbs	19	31	50
Radio	31	32	63
Iron	28	29	57
Television	12	9	21
Refrigerator	19	8	27
Washing machine	10	4	14
Water pump	12	4	16
Incubator	1	--	1
Sewing machine	1	--	1
Stove	1	1	2
Security alarm	1	--	1
Utility motors:			
1/2 HP	4	--	4
1 HP	5	1	6
1 1/2 HP	10	4	14
2 HP	5	9	14
3 HP	2	5	7
5 HP	--	4	4
50 HP	--	2	2

Source: Community Survey.

Respondents in Sevilla intended to purchase 26 utility motors while those in Caicedonia intended to purchase 25. There was some difference, however, in the size of the motors. Respondents in Sevilla indicated they would purchase smaller motors than did the respondents in Caicedonia. This is primarily because the farms were smaller in Sevilla and the motors were to be used almost entirely for dispulping coffee beans. Some respondents, however, were intending to use the motors for cutting sugar cane to feed to their livestock, and the exceptionally large motors were to be used in sugar cane operations. The differences in the intended uses of electricity for one year and three years are shown in Table 41.

Anticipated Benefits and Costs

To determine if the potential rural consumers had thought about the beneficial effects and economic aspects of electrification they were asked questions concerning anticipated benefits and expected cost of electricity.

Almost all of the respondents (94 percent) thought that their intended uses of electricity would provide some benefits. Three of the respondents said they did not know. Ninety percent of the respondents said electricity would save them time. Sixty percent of the sample said electricity would provide them with more security. One respondent was planning to install a security alarm system, while the others were expecting to improve their security with electric lights. "Mas seguridad, medio de seguridad," or "mas seguridad en la cosecha," ("more security, means of security" or "more security during harvesting") were the most frequently mentioned comments.

Half of the sample thought electricity would reduce the cost of their present operations. Thus, the three benefits mentioned by 50 percent or more of the respondents were that electricity will (1) save time, (2) provide more security, and (3) reduce the cost of present operations.

TABLE 41

Differences in Intended Uses of Electricity
among 50 Farms According to Time
of Availability, 1965

Use	1 Year	3 Years	Differ.
Incandescent bulbs (house)	588	707	119
Incandescent bulbs (other)	164	399	235
Fluorescent tubes	50	86	36
Infrared bulbs	26	50	24
Radio	50	63	13
Iron	55	57	2
Television	8	21	13
Refrigerator	17	27	10
Washing machine	7	14	7
Water pump	9	16	7
Incubator	1	1	1
Sewing machine	1	1	1
Stove	--	2	2
Security alarm	--	1	1
Utility motors:			
1/2 HP	4	4	--
1 HP	5	6	1
1 1/2 HP	9	14	5
2 HP	10	14	4
3 HP	6	7	1
5 HP	2	4	2
50 HP	2	2	--

Source: Consumer Survey.

Six percent of the sample said electricity
would make it possible for them to increase their
production, although a considerably larger percentage intended to increase production. Six percent
said the rural electric cooperative would provide
them with a more reliable source of power. One
farm was receiving power from the existing system
in Sevilla and the owner said the energy "llega
cansada," which means that the energy arrives tired.

He was using electricity from Sevilla only for
lighting and produced energy with a diesel plant
to operate his sugar cane operations. One respondent thought electricity would increase his income
and another thought it would increase the value of
his farm. Anticipated benefits of electricity according to the number of respondents are shown in
Table 42.

Respondents also were asked if they expected
to pay more, less or the same for electricity from
the rural electric cooperative than they had been
paying for the fuels or power that it would replace
(see Table 43). Thirty-six percent of the sample
thought they would pay less; however, an equal percentage said they did not know. Twenty-two percent
thought electricity would cost them more and 6 percent said it would cost about the same. In Caicedonia opinion was the opposite of that in Sevilla;
four times as many respondents thought electricity
would cost less as thought it would cost more.
Other opinions were about the same for the two
municipios.

TABLE 42

Anticipated Benefits of Electricity
among 50 Respondents in Sevilla
and Caicedonia, 1965

Benefit	Sevilla	Caicedonia	Total
Save time	22	23	45
Provide security	13	17	30
Reduce costs	10	15	25
Increase production	1	2	3
More reliable source	2	1	3
Increase income	1	--	1
Increase value of farm	--	1	1

Source: Consumer Survey.

TABLE 43

Opinions on Anticipated Costs of Electricity
among 50 Respondents in Sevilla
and Caicedonia, 1965

Opinion	Sevilla	Caicedonia	Total
More	8	3	11
Less	6	12	18
Same	1	2	3
Do not know	10	8	18

Source: Consumer Survey.

It was evident that not many of the respondents had thought about the anticipated cost of electricity in terms of a specific amount of money. Those who replied that they thought electricity would cost them more or less than the fuels or power that it would replace were asked how much more or less. Of the 29 respondents asked this question, 25 said they did not know. The three respondents who thought it would cost more and the one who thought it would cost less gave specific amounts. The three who thought it would cost more said it would cost 1, 4 and 20 pesos per month more. The respondent who thought it would cost less said it would cost 11 pesos per month less.

Those respondents who said it would cost more were asked how they expected to pay this additional monthly cost. Eight said they would take money from their savings to pay the added costs, six said they would increase production, one said he would obtain additional work and one said he did not know.

Previous Electrification

When asked if they had electric power on their farm, ten respondents in Sevilla and ten respondents in Caicedonia said they did, although one of the

power units in Caicedonia was broken. Therefore,
only 40 percent of those interviewed were using
electric power either from private generating
plants or from the existing system in Sevilla. Two
other respondents had purchased electricity previously from a neighbor's private plant, but it was
no longer available.

The number of hours each day that electricity
was being used by the respondents varied from 2 to
24 (see Table 44). Of the four respondents who had
electricity available for 24 hours, three were purchasing power from the existing Sevilla system and
one was generating it himself.

All except one respondent used the electricity
for lights in the home and in connection with their
farm operations. The respondent who was the exception did not have lights in his home but used the
privately generated electricity entirely for his
poultry operations. Radios and electric irons were
each owned by eight respondents. Two of the respondents had television sets and two had record players. The uses of electricity were as shown in
Table 45.

Respondents were asked how much the electricity
cost them each month. The estimated costs varied
from 8 pesos to 380 pesos (see Table 46). The highest estimate was by a respondent who was operating
two generating plants an average of ten hours per
day. He used the plants in connection with his
sugar cane operations. The next highest estimated
bill was by the operator of a trapiche who used
power purchased from Sevilla only for lighting. He
said his monthly light bill averaged 300 pesos.
The smallest bill also was for a respondent using
power from the Sevilla system. The average monthly
bill for lights and an electric iron was 8 pesos.

One respondent was using privately generated
power at virtually no cost. The family long ago had
purchased materials and constructed a small hydroelectric plant. The force of a mountain stream was
being used to provide lighting and to dispulp coffee
beans.

TABLE 44

Power Availability by Number
of Consumers, 1965

Hours Available	Sevilla	Caicedonia	Total
2	1	2	3
3	2	3	5
4	4	1	5
6	1	--	1
10	--	1	1
12	--	1	1
24	2	2	4
Total:	10	10	20

Source: Consumer Survey.

TABLE 45

Present Use of Electricity among
20 Respondents, 1965

Use	Sevilla	Caicedonia	Total
Home lighting	10	9	19
Iron	6	2	8
Radio	5	3	8
Television	2	--	2
Record player	2	--	2
Coffee operation	--	1	1
Poultry operation	--	1	1
Sugar cane operation	--	2	2

Source: Consumer Survey.

TABLE 46

Estimated Average Monthly Costs of Electricity among 20 Respondents

Cost	Sevilla	Caicedonia	Total
Less than 50 pesos	7	4	11
From 50 to 100 pesos	2	2	4
100 pesos and more	1	4	5

Source: Consumer Survey.

Farm Size, Ownership and Land Use

Farm size varied from 3.2 hectares to 1,280 hectares in Sevilla. In Caicedonia farm size varied from 2.6 hectares to 326 hectares. More than half of the farms (56 percent) were operated by the owners. Of the remaining farms, 32 percent had administrators and 12 percent were operated by persons renting the land. Use of the land was predominantly for growing coffee and platano often was grown on the same land. Pasture, primarily for beef and dairy cattle, was the next most important land use. Other land was used for sugar cane, yuca, corn, beans and cacao.

Farm size in hectares and land use for each of the respondents are shown in Table 47. Farms 1 through 25 were located in Sevilla; farms 26 through 50 were located in Caicedonia.

The average size of the farms surveyed in Caicedonia was 66.4 hectares. Not including those farms over 200 hectares gave an average size of 38.7 hectares. About half of the farms surveyed in Sevilla ranged in size from 5 to less than 20

TABLE 47

Farm Size and Land Use on 50 Farms in Sevilla and Caicedonia, 1965
(in hectares)

Farm	Coffee	Pasture	Other Crops	Waste	Total
1	4.5	--	--	--	4.5
2	28.2	2.5	--	--	30.7
3	22.4	6.4	--	--	28.8
4	11.5	--	--	--	11.5
5	6.4	--	--	--	6.4
6	9.6	--	--	--	9.6
7	51.2	12.8	--	--	64.0
8	5.8	1.9	--	--	7.7
9	9.6	64.0	--	3.2	76.8
10	--	1,246.1	1.9	32.0	1,280.0
11	10.9	60.8	--	--	71.7
12	4.5	1.9	--	--	6.4
13	25.0	7.0	--	--	32.0
14	19.2	14.7	4.5	--	38.4
15	5.1	--	--	4.5	9.6
16	3.2	--	--	--	3.2
17	7.0	1.9	1.3	--	10.2
18	12.8	--	--	--	12.8
19	51.2	--	--	--	51.2
20	7.0	1.9	2.6	1.3	12.8
21	10.3	.6	--	--	10.9
22	10.9	1.3	--	--	12.2
23	6.4	1.3	--	--	7.7
24	2.6	1.9	--	--	4.5

25	1.9	--	--	1.9	3.8
26	19.2	2.0	.6	.6	22.4
27	192.0	11.5	--	--	203.5
28	127.4	--	.6	--	128.0
29	64.0	2.6	7.6	2.6	76.8
30	18.6	.6	--	1.3	20.5
31	6.4	.3	1.0	--	7.7
32	2.0	--	.6	--	2.6
33	7.1	--	.6	--	7.7
34	--	76.8	182.4	19.2	278.4
35	7.7	234.2	58.9	25.6	326.4
36	38.4	25.6	--	--	64.0
37	6.4	--	1.3	--	7.7
38	44.8	--	--	6.4	51.2
39	16.0	.7	--	3.8	20.5
40	16.0	3.2	--	--	19.2
41	22.4	3.2	--	--	25.6
42	140.8	9.6	--	9.6	160.0
43	25.0	3.2	--	.6	28.8
44	9.0	1.2	--	--	10.2
45	64.0	3.2	--	9.6	76.8
46	5.1	--	--	--	5.1
47	25.0	.6	--	--	25.6
48	28.2	1.9	1.3	--	31.4
49	50.6	.6	--	--	51.2
50	9.0	1.0	--	.2	10.2
Total:	1,273.3	1,809.0	265.2	122.4	3,468.9

Source: Consumer Survey.

hectares. The average size farm for those surveyed
in Sevilla was 72.3 hectares. Not including the
exceptionally large farm, the average size was 22.0
hectares. The only large farm in the sample used
almost all of its land for pasture. It was the only
one among 25 sampled that did not have some land in
coffee.

Distribution of farms surveyed in Sevilla and
Caicedonia by size is shown in Table 48. The number of hectares in each distribution class according to the size of the farm sampled is shown in
Table 49.

TABLE 48

Number and Area of Farms Surveyed
in Sevilla and Caicedonia, 1965

No. of Hectares	No. of Farms	Total Area
Sevilla:		
Less than 5	4	16.0
5-19.9	12	117.8
20-99.9	8	393.6
100 and over	1	1,280.0
Total:	25	1,807.4
Caicedonia:		
Less than 5	1	2.6
5-19.9	7	67.9
20-99.9	12	492.8
100 and over	5	1,096.3
Total:	25	1,659.6

Source: Consumer Survey.

TABLE 49

Number of Hectares and Type of Tenancy
for Each Group Size among
50 Farms Surveyed, 1965

No. of Hectares			
Less than 5	5-19.9	20-99.9	100 & Over
Sevilla:			
4.5^a	11.5^b	30.7^a	$1,280.0^a$
3.2^a	6.4^a	28.8^a	
4.5^b	9.6^a	64.0^b	
$\underline{3.8}^a$	7.7^b	71.7^a	
16.0	6.4^a	32.0^a	
	9.6^a	38.4^a	
	10.2^a	51.2^c	
	12.8^a	$\underline{76.8}^b$	
	12.8^c	393.6	
	10.9^a		
	12.2^a		
	$\underline{7.7}^a$		
	117.8		
Caicedonia:			
2.6^a	7.7^a	22.4^a	203.5^a
	7.7^b	25.6^a	278.4^a
	7.7^b	76.2^a	326.4^b
	19.2^b	20.5^c	128.0^b
	10.2^b	64.0^b	$\underline{160.0}^c$
	5.1^a	51.2^b	1,096.3
	$\underline{10.3}^a$	20.4^c	
	67.9	28.8^a	
		76.8^b	
		25.6^a	
		30.1^b	
		$\underline{51.2}^c$	
		492.8	

[a]Owner operating farm.

[b]Administrator operating farm.

[c]Renter operating farm.

Source: Consumer Survey.

More of the farms in Sevilla than in Caicedonia
were being operated by owners. Part of the reason
for this is that the violence was more prominent in
Caicedonia and the owners have not returned to their
land as quickly as in Sevilla. Renting in both
municipios was least popular of the three methods
of farm operation. The number of farms by type of
operation in Sevilla and Caicedonia is shown in
Table 50.

In the combined sample, farms being operated
by owners outnumbered those being operated by administrators 2 to 1. Owner-operated farms in
Sevilla accounted for 36 percent while those in
Caicedonia accounted for 20 percent of the total.

TABLE 50

Number of Farms by Type of Tenancy
and Size, 1965

No. of Hectares	Owner	Administrator	Renter
Sevilla:			
Less than 5	3	1	--
5-19.9	9	2	1
20-199.9	5	2	1
200 and over	1	--	--
Subtotal:	18	5	2
Caicedonia:			
Less than 5	1	--	--
5-19.9	3	4	--
20-199.9	4	6	4
200 and over	2	1	--
Subtotal:	10	11	4
Total:	28	16	6

Source: Consumer Survey.

Respondent Information

Most of the respondents were in the 30 and 40 year age groups. Six out of 50 were in their 20's and one respondent was 90 years old. There was little difference in the ages of those interviewed in Sevilla and those questioned in Caicedonia. Ages of the respondents are shown in Table 51.

Thirty of the respondents had less than 6 dependents each while 20 respondents each had more than 6. Total number of dependents for the 30 respondents, however, was less than the total for the 20 respondents. Total number of dependents for the 50 respondents was 303. The average was slightly more than 6 dependents for each farm interviewed. The number of respondents having less than 7 dependents and the number having 7 or more are shown in Table 52.

TABLE 51

Ages of Respondents in Sevilla and
Caicedonia, 1965

| Age | No. of Respondents | | |
	Sevilla	Caicedonia	Total
29 and under	2	4	6
30 to 39	9	8	17
40 to 49	7	7	14
50 to 59	4	2	6
60 to 69	1	1	2
70 to 79	2	1	3
80 to 89	–	1	1
90 and over	–	1	1

Source: Consumer Survey.

TABLE 52

Number of Respondents Classified by
Number of Dependents, 1965

| Classification | No. of Dependents | | |
	Sevilla	Caicedonia	Total
Six dependents or less	12	18	30
Seven dependents or more	13	7	20

Source: Consumer Survey.

Total number of dependents for the respondents classified by the number of dependents is shown in Table 53.

Only one respondent among the 50 interviewed had gone to school beyond secondary school, and he had completed 12 years of school. Only 11 respondents had completed 6 years or more of school. Primary school in Colombia includes grades 1 through 5. Secondary school includes grades 6 through 11. After secondary school the students are prepared for university work.

An equal number of respondents in Sevilla as in Caicedonia, six, had completed primary school and taken some work in the secondary school. The number of respondents and the school they were attending when they stopped their formal education are shown in Table 54. Total number of school years completed by the respondents according to the schools they were attending is shown in Table 55.

Thus, a total of 38 respondents or 76 percent of the sample completed 78 years of school. The remaining 12 respondents or 24 percent of the sample completed 105 years of school. The total sample of 50 completed 183 years of school, making the average

TABLE 53

Number of Dependents among
50 Respondents, 1965

Classification	No. of Dependents		
	Sevilla	Caicedonia	Total
Respondents with less than 7 dependents	45	62	107
Respondents with 7 or more dependents	125	71	196
Total number of dependents	170	133	303

Source: Consumer Survey.

TABLE 54

Number of Respondents According to
Type of School Last Attended, 1965

Type of School	No. of Respondents		
	Sevilla	Caicedonia	Total
Primary school	19	19	38
Secondary school	5	6	11
University	1	--	1
Total:	25	25	50

Source: Consumer Survey.

TABLE 55

Number of School Years Completed
by 50 Respondents, 1965

| Type of School | No. of Respondents | | |
	Sevilla	Caicedonia	Total
Primary school	45	3	78
Secondary school	46	47	93
University	12	--	12
Total:	103	80	183

Source: Consumer Survey.

education for each respondent 3.7 years. In Sevilla
the average was slightly more than 4 years of school
while in Caicedonia it was approximately one year
less.

Respondents were asked how they judged their
reading ability. Whether it was good, fair, poor
or they could not read. Forty percent said "regular" or fair, 34 percent said good, 14 percent said
poor and 12 percent said they could not read. There
was little difference between Sevilla and Caicedonia
except that there were more respondents in Caicedonia who said they could not read. This is consistent with the fewer years of school completed by the
respondents in Caicedonia. The estimated reading
abilities of the respondents were as shown in Table
56.

More than half of the respondents said they belonged to a community organization. Thirty-six percent belonged to the Cooperativa de Caficultores,
the coffee growers cooperative, and 26 percent belonged to the various Juntas de Accion Comunal,

community action groups. Two respondents, or 4 percent, were members of school boards. Table 57
shows organization membership.

A considerably larger number of respondents in
Sevilla belonged to organizations than did respondents in Caicedonia. This can be attributed partly
to the fact that more coffee growers were interviewed in Sevilla than in Caicedonia. The coffee
cooperative had an office only in Sevilla until
1964 when they opened one in Caicedonia. Also, the
Juntas de Accion Comunal have been emphasized more
in Sevilla than in Caicedonia. This is despite the
fact that Juntas seem to be more successful in
Caicedonia. Peace Corps Volunteers in Sevilla have
been working with the various communities to organize Juntas. Because of the violence throughout the
area, there were no volunteers located in Caicedonia.
Thus Peace Corps assistance may have resulted in
more Juntas being formed in Sevilla.

TABLE 56

Reading Abilities of 50 Respondents in
Sevilla and Caicedonia, 1965

| Reading Ability | No. of Respondents | | |
	Sevilla	Caicedonia	Total
Good	9	8	17
Fair	10	10	20
Poor	5	2	7
None	1	5	6

Source: Consumer Survey.

TABLE 57

Organization Membership of
50 Respondents, 1965

Organization	No. of Respondents		
	Sevilla	Caicedonia	Total
Cooperativa de Caficultores	12	6	18
Junta de Accion Comunal	9	4	13
Local School Board	--	2	2
Total:	21	12	33

Source: Consumer Survey.

Educational Facilities

Teachers of six schools in the electric cooperative area were asked the intended uses of electricity at the schools and other selected questions from
the Consumer Survey form.

Intended use of electricity in the rural
schools was primarily for lighting in the classrooms and for improving living conditions of the
teachers residing at the schools (see Table 58).
It was estimated by the teachers interviewed that
the schools would use a total of 77 light bulbs or
an average of better than 12 bulbs per school within
three years after electricity became available.
Among the six schools surveyed, all but one had
facilities for the teachers to live at the school.
Four actually lived at the schools.

One teacher thought the school would purchase
a refrigerator and another said the school would
install an electric water pump. There was no water

at the school, although the teacher was living there.
In order to obtain water, she had to use a neighbor's source.

One school, San Isidro, at Montegrande had a
small generating plant used by the teacher in her
living quarters. None of the other schools had
electricity.

The teacher at San Isidro lived at the school
with her husband and four children. Her husband
was a tailor and also ran a small general store at
the school. Electricity from the small plant was
used only for lighting for about two hours each
evening. The estimated cost was Col $10.50 monthly.

TABLE 58

Anticipated Use of Electricity among
Six Rural Schools, 1965

Anticipated Use	Rural School						Total No. of Appliances
	a	b	c	d	e	f	
Bulbs	7	14	12	20	19	5	77
Radio	--	1	--	1	1	1	4
Iron	1	1	1	1	1	1	6
Television	1	1	--	1	1	--	4
Refrigerator	1	--	--	--	--	--	1
Water pump	--	1	--	--	--	--	1

Source: Consumer Survey.

Five of the six schools intended to begin evening classes for adults after electricity became available. Classes would teach reading, writing and arithmetic. They would be held from 7 to 9 p.m. Monday through Friday. The teacher at Puerto Rico also expressed hope in having music classes in the evenings.

Five of the teachers said electricity would improve living conditions at the schools. The sixth school at El Crucero was old and did not have living facilities. The schoolteacher at Canoas said that during the dry seasons water was not available at the school. She thought the school might install a pump but was not sure.

Four of the six schools had been built by the Coffee Federation. They were modern buildings and were completely wired for electricity. The other two schools, at Canoas and Crucero, were older buildings that had been built by the government. In some cases the salaries of the teachers were paid by the Coffee Federation and in other cases they were paid by the government.

The number of classrooms, number of students and years of school taught at each school were as shown in Table 59. The teachers had completed an average of 8 years of school and were relatively young. Their age, years of school completed, number of dependents and marital status were as shown in Table 60.

BENCH MARK DATA

To provide bench marks from which a follow-up study could measure change the 50 respondents were asked questions concerning input, output, income, cooperative knowledge and values and attitudes. This information was then quantified to provide bench mark data.

TABLE 59

Number of Classrooms, Students and Years of
School Taught at Six Rural Schools, 1965

School	Classrooms	Students	Years of School
a	2	35	2
b	3	110	3
c	3	106	5
d	2	38	3
e	1	35	2
f	2	33	2
Total:	13	357	

Source: Consumer Survey.

TABLE 60

Age, Years of School, Number of Dependents
and Marital Status of Teachers at Six
Rural Schools, 1965

Item	Teachers at Rural School					
	a	b	c	d	e	f
Age	20	22	34	28	19	38
Years of school	6	8	8	8	9	9
No. of dependents	8	--	--	10	4	4
Marital status	S	S	M	M	S	M

Source: Consumer Survey.

Base Period Input

The value of 1964 input for the farms surveyed
in Sevilla varied from Col $1,346 to Col $155,709.
Hired labor was by far the most important input.
Only on one farm in Sevilla did the value of other
inputs exceed that of hired labor.

Energy inputs were used almost entirely for
dispulping coffee and providing lights for the home.
All farms used energy in some manner for lighting
and more than half used it for dispulping coffee.
Of the 24 farms producing coffee, 10 dispulped the
beans by using hand labor. In some cases privately
generated power was used for other electrical appliances. One farm also used energy for pumping water
and another farm used fuel for heating baby chicks.

Costs for variable inputs were incurred by 14
of the 25 farms in Sevilla. Fertilizer, primarily
for coffee, was the most important. Of the 14
farms, 13 purchased fertilizer. The remaining respondent operated a beef cattle farm and incurred
expenses for feed. Two other farms also purchased
feed, one for poultry and the other for swine.

Only one farm purchased seed in 1964. This
was a small amount of seed corn. Two other respondents purchased insecticides for their coffee crops.

The value of farm input in 1964 for Caicedonia
varied from Col $3,143 to Col $460,080. Both figures were higher in Caicedonia than in Sevilla.
Again hired labor was the input with the highest
value. Only two farms had other inputs that were
valued higher than labor. On the remaining farms
the value of hired labor exceeded the value of all
other inputs combined.

Energy inputs were used for more varied purposes in Caicedonia than in Sevilla, although energy was used primarily for lighting and dispulping
coffee beans. Other uses included energy for producing panela, drying coffee, operating refrigerators,

cutting sugar cane for feed, heating baby chicks and pumping water.

All but three farms incurred costs for variable inputs. As in Sevilla the most important of these inputs was fertilizer. Of the 25 farms surveyed, 22 used fertilizer. Feed was the next most important item. Other inputs included seed corn, seed beans, and cacao trees. Value of 1964 inputs for the 50 farms surveyed in Sevilla and Caicedonia is shown in Table 61.

Although there were two less private power units operating in Caicedonia at the time of the study, the total costs for private power generation was considerably higher in Caicedonia than in Sevilla. This resulted primarily because of the larger farms surveyed in Caicedonia and the greater use of electric power in the farming operations.

Gasoline expenditures for gas lamps were about twice as high in Caicedonia as in Sevilla. Annual costs for candles were only slightly higher. A trapiche in Caicedonia located near the existing Sevilla distribution system was paying Col $3,000 annually for power that was used only for lighting. Two consumers in Sevilla were paying much less.

Of the 50 farms surveyed, 22 were using gas lamps; candles were used by 29. The average annual cost for these 29 farms for candles was Col $120. This was an average cost of $10 per month for candle light. For 12 of the farms, candles were the sole source of light.

Because energy from the private power plants was also used for other appliances such as radios, irons, record players, television sets and utility motors it was difficult to separate lighting costs for the entire sample. Leaving out 14 farms that were operating private power plants for lights at the time of the survey, gave an average annual cost of Col $253 for the remaining 36 farms.

TABLE 61

Value of Base Inputs for 50 Farms
in Sevilla and Caicedonia, 1964
(in pesos)

Farm	Hired Labor	Energy	Other	Total
1	39,312	127	17,324	56,763
2	140,400	309	15,000	155,709
3	70,200	293	--	70,493
4	18,720	845	660	20,225
5	14,400	153	3,180	17,733
6	14,400	90	240	14,730
7	90,000	832	6,600	97,432
8	5,440	548	2,280	8,268
9	2,600	156	440	3,196
10	49,920	773	10,400	61,093
11	20,640	825	--	21,465
12	3,600	823	2,300	6,723
13	27,930	358	--	28,288
14	7,500	603	--	8,103
15	2,550	128	--	2,678
16	1,500	104	--	1,604
17	975	244	255	1,474
18	18,000	120	--	18,120
19	42,240	766	--	43,006
20	5,400	104	--	5,504
21	18,000	303	2,750	21,053
22	23,040	444	1,500	24,984
23	3,000	96	825	3,921
24	1,200	156	2,032	3,388
25	1,200	146	--	1,346

Farm	Hired Labor	Energy	Other	Total
26	16,110	420	2,220	18,750
27	449,280	10,800	--	460,080
28	180,000	426	2,120	182,546
29	90,000	3,789	5,500	99,289
30	21,600	423	2,200	24,223
31	15,964	834	2,450	19,248
32	2,880	144	119	3,143
33	12,960	132	990	14,082
34	162,000	46,696	37,400	246,096
35	194,100	26,623	30,970	251,693
36	75,000	858	--	75,858
37	2,250	656	3,850	6,756
38	20,520	78	960	21,558
39	20,160	320	6,600	27,080
40	11,200	236	920	12,356
41	4,320	247	893	5,460
42	121,600	1,797	2,200	125,597
43	4,000	1,092	26,380	31,472
44	27,200	154	1,200	28,554
45	14,400	234	14,440	29,074
46	8,000	166	500	8,666
47	86,400	856	9,712	96,968
48	12,600	575	2,793	15,968
49	56,320	375	2,750	59,445
50	15,000	283	--	15,283
Total:	2,246,031	107,560	222,953	2,576,544

Source: Consumer Survey.

For the entire sample, the average annual cost for lighting and use of electric appliances was Col $381. The average monthly cost was Col $32. Value of energy for lighting is shown in Table 62.

Dividing production inputs by the number of hectares in each farm gave the input per hectare. Average value of production inputs per hectare for the 25 farms in Sevilla was Col $386; in Caicedonia, Col $1,131; and for the entire sample, Col $743. Input per hectare for each farm surveyed is shown in Table 63.

Value of labor input per hectare is shown in Table 64. Energy input per hectare in terms of Colombian pesos is shown in Table 65. Application of fertilizer per hectare of coffee on each farm is shown in Table 66.

The greatest relative difference in the value of inputs among the respondents in Sevilla and those in Caicedonia was the energy inputs. Average total inputs were valued almost four times greater in Caicedonia than in Sevilla. The value of labor input per hectare was almost three times greater in Caicedonia, but the value of energy input per hectare was over seven times greater than in Sevilla.

Base Period Output

Coffee was produced and sold by 24 of the 25 farms interviewed in Sevilla. It was the only product sold in the market for 12 of the farms. Platano was produced and sold by 9 farms; 1 farm sold poultry and eggs; 1 sold milk; 2 sold beef; 3 sold yuca; and 1 sold pork.

Only on one farm was there any member of the family earning off-farm income. The son of the farm operator taught at the local school. He was paid 500 pesos per month for a 12-month year. None of the family members of those interviewed in Caicedonia earned an income off the farm.

TABLE 62

Value of Energy for Lighting of 50 Farms
in Sevilla and Caicedonia, 1964
(in pesos)

Farm	Power Unit*	Gas Lamp	Candles	Sevilla System	Total
1	--	38	--	--	38
2	180	--	--	--	180
3	--	148	--	--	148
4	626	96	--	--	722
5	--	--	96	--	96
6	--	--	60	--	60
7	572	--	--	--	572
8	514	--	--	--	514
9	--	--	156	--	156
10	358	--	--	--	358
11	495	--	--	--	495
12	490	--	--	--	490
13	--	180	--	--	180
14	--	276	192	--	468
15	--	24	104	--	128
16	--	--	104	--	104
17	--	48	156	--	204
18	--	--	120	--	120
19	486	--	--	--	486
20	--	--	104	--	104
21	--	--	--	180	180
22	--	154	192	--	346
23	--	--	96	--	96
24	--	--	156	--	156
25	--	--	50	96	146

(Continued)

TABLE 62 (Continued)

Farm	Power Unit*	Gas Lamp	Candles	Sevilla System	Total
26	--	24	240	--	264
27	--	--	--	--	--
28	--	--	240	--	240
29	3,420	--	--	--	3,420
30	--	48	96	--	144
31	357	96	48	--	501
32	--	48	96	--	144
33	--	--	96	--	96
34	--	--	--	3,000	3,000
35	438	--	--	--	438
36	--	250	--	--	250
37	--	360	--	--	360
38	--	--	36	--	36
39	--	48	120	--	168
40	--	46	42	--	88
41	--	48	156	--	204
42	1,020	--	96	--	1,116
43	--	120	96	--	216
44	--	104	--	--	104
45	240	--	--	--	240
46	--	114	52	--	166
47	--	387	208	--	595
48	387	--	--	--	387
49	--	48	156	--	204
50	--	--	108	--	108
Total	9,583	2,705	3,472	3,276	190,036

*Includes cost of power generated to operate other appliances.

Source: Consumer Survey.

TABLE 63

Input per Hectare for Each Farm
Surveyed, 1964

Farm	Total Input (Col $)	Hectares	Input per Hectare (Col $)
1	56,763	4.5	12,614
2	155,709	30.7	5,072
3	70,493	28.8	2,448
4	20,225	11.5	1,759
5	17,733	6.4	2,771
6	14,730	9.6	1,534
7	97,432	64.0	1,522
8	8,268	7.7	1,074
9	3,196	76.8	42
10	61,093	1,280.0	48
11	21,465	71.7	299
12	6,723	6.4	1,050
13	28,288	32.0	884
14	8,103	38.4	211
15	2,678	9.6	279
16	1,604	3.2	501
17	1,474	10.2	145
18	18,120	12.8	1,416
19	43,006	51.2	840
20	5,504	12.8	430
21	21,053	10.9	1,931
22	24,984	12.2	2,048
23	3,921	7.7	509
24	3,388	4.5	753
25	1,346	3.8	354

(Continued)

TABLE 63 (Continued)

Farm	Total Input (Col $)	Hectares	Input per Hectare (Col $)
26	18,750	22.4	837
27	460,080	203.5	2,261
28	182,546	128.0	1,426
29	99,289	76.8	1,293
30	24,223	20.5	1,182
31	19,248	7.7	2,500
32	3,143	2.6	1,209
33	14,082	7.7	1,829
34	246,096	278.4	884
35	251,693	326.4	771
36	75,858	64.0	1,185
37	6,756	7.7	877
38	21,558	51.2	421
39	27,080	20.5	1,321
40	12,356	19.2	644
41	5,460	25.6	213
42	125,597	160.0	785
43	31,472	28.8	1,093
44	28,554	10.2	2,799
45	29,074	76.8	380
46	8,666	5.1	1,699
47	96,968	25.6	3,788
48	15,968	21.4	509
49	59,445	51.2	1,161
50	15,283	10.2	1,498
Total	2,576,544	3,468.9	743

Source: Consumer Survey.

TABLE 64

Value of Labor Input per Hectare of Land for
50 Farms in Sevilla and Caicedonia, 1964

Farm	Labor (Col $)	Hectares	Labor Input per Hectare (Col $)
1	39,312	4.5	8,736
2	140,400	30.7	4,573
3	70,200	28.8	2,438
4	18,720	11.5	1,628
5	14,400	6.4	2,250
6	14,400	9.6	1,500
7	90,000	64.0	1,406
8	5,440	7.7	706
9	2,600	76.8	34
10	49,920	1,280.0	39
11	20,640	71.7	288
12	3,600	6.4	563
13	27,930	32.0	873
14	7,500	38.4	195
15	2,550	9.6	266
16	1,500	3.2	469
17	975	10.2	96
18	18,000	12.8	1,406
19	42,240	51.2	825
20	5,400	12.8	422
21	18,000	10.9	1,651
22	23,040	12.2	1,889
23	3,000	7.7	390
24	1,200	4.5	267
25	1,200	3.8	316

(Continued)

TABLE 64 (Continued)

Farm	Labor (Col $)	Hectares	Labor Input per Hectare (Col $)
26	16,110	22.4	719
27	449,280	203.5	2,208
28	180,000	128.0	1,406
29	90,000	76.8	1,172
30	21,600	20.5	1,054
31	15,964	7.7	2,073
32	2,880	2.6	1,108
33	12,960	7.7	1,683
34	162,000	278.4	582
35	194,100	326.4	595
36	75,000	64.0	1,172
37	2,250	7.7	292
38	20,520	51.2	401
39	20,160	20.5	983
40	11,200	19.2	583
41	4,320	25.6	169
42	121,600	160.0	760
43	4,000	28.8	139
44	27,200	10.2	2,667
45	14,400	76.8	188
46	8,000	5.1	1,569
47	86,400	25.1	3,375
48	12,600	31.4	401
49	56,320	51.2	1,100
50	15,000	10.2	1,471
Total:	2,246,031	3,468.9	647

Source: Consumer Survey.

TABLE 65

Value of Energy Input per Hectare for 50 Farms in Sevilla and Caicedonia, 1964

Farm	Energy (Col $)	Hectares	Energy Input per Hectare (Col $)
1	127	4.5	28
2	309	30.7	10
3	293	28.8	10
4	845	11.5	73
5	153	6.4	24
6	90	9.6	9
7	832	64.0	13
8	548	7.7	71
9	156	76.8	2
10	773	1,280.0	1
11	825	71.7	12
12	823	6.4	129
13	358	32.0	11
14	603	38.4	16
15	128	9.6	13
16	104	3.2	33
17	244	10.2	24
18	120	12.8	9
19	766	51.2	15
20	104	12.8	8
21	303	10.9	28
22	444	12.2	36
23	96	7.7	12
24	156	4.5	35
25	146	3.8	38

(Continued)

TABLE 65 (Continued)

Farm	Energy (Col $)	Hectares	Energy Input per Hectare (Col $)
26	420	22.4	19
27	10,800	203.5	53
28	426	128.0	3
29	3,789	76.8	49
30	423	20.5	21
31	834	7.7	108
32	144	2.6	55
33	132	7.7	17
34	46,969	278.4	168
35	26,623	326.4	82
36	858	64.0	13
37	656	7.7	85
38	78	51.2	2
39	320	20.5	16
40	236	19.2	12
41	247	25.6	10
42	1,797	160.0	11
43	1,092	28.8	38
44	154	10.2	15
45	234	76.8	3
46	166	5.1	33
47	856	25.6	33
48	575	31.4	18
49	375	51.2	7
50	283	10.2	28
Total:	107,560	3,468.9	31

Source: Consumer Survey.

TABLE 66

Application of Fertilizer in Bultos per
Hectare of Coffee Land on 50 Farms in
Sevilla and Caicedonia, 1964

Farm	Bultos of Fertilizer	No. of Hectares	Bultos per Hectare
1	60	4.5	13.3
2	200	28.2	7.1
3	--	22.4	--
4	12	11.5	1.0
5	60	6.4	9.4
6	10	9.6	1.0
7	120	51.2	2.3
8	40	5.8	6.9
9	8	9.6	.8
10	--	--	--
11	--	10.9	--
12	40	4.5	8.9
13	--	25.0	--
14	--	19.2	--
15	--	5.1	--
16	--	3.2	--
17	--	7.0	--
18	--	12.8	--
19	--	51.2	--
20	--	7.0	--
21	50	10.3	4.9
22	27	10.9	2.5
23	15	6.4	2.3
24	18	2.6	6.9
25	--	1.9	--

(Continued)

TABLE 66 (Continued)

Farm	Bultos of Fertilizer	No. of Hectares	Bultos per Hectare
26	40	19.2	2.1
27	--	192.0	--
28	40	127.4	.3
29	100	64.0	1.6
30	40	18.6	2.2
31	40	6.4	6.3
32	2	2.0	1.0
33	18	7.1	2.5
34	--	--	--
35	--	7.7	--
36	--	38.4	--
37	70	6.4	10.9
38	16	44.8	.4
39	120	16.0	7.5
40	20	16.0	1.3
41	14	22.4	.6
42	40	140.8	.3
43	100	25.0	4.0
44	18	9.0	2.0
45	250	64.0	3.9
46	10	5.1	2.0
47	160	25.0	6.4
48	50	28.2	1.8
49	50	50.6	1.0
50	--	9.0	--
Total:	1,858	1,272.3	1.5

Source: Consumer Survey.

As in Sevilla, coffee was produced and sold by 24 of the 25 farms surveyed in Caicedonia. However, 10 farms in Caicedonia produced only coffee as opposed to 12 in Sevilla. Other farm products sold in the market included panela, cacao, platano, eggs, poultry, milk, corn and beef.

Value of 1964 output for each of the 50 farms surveyed is shown in Table 67. In Table 68 the value of output per hectare is shown. Coffee yields in arrobas per hectare are shown in Table 69. Average coffee yield was slightly higher in Caicedonia, 61 arrobas per hectare as compared to 52 in Sevilla. Sources of farm output are shown in Table 70. Coffee was by far the major source of income on the 50 farms.

Base Value Added

Base value added by the farms to the GNP was computed by subtracting production inputs not contributed by the farms from the gross output of the farms. The formula was: Gross output - production inputs = Farm's addition to GNP.

For the 50 farms making up the sample in the cooperative area, the value added was determined by subtracting labor, energy and variable inputs from the value of farm products marketed. The result is referred to as base value added. Letting G equal gross output, L equal labor, E equal energy, Vi equal variable inputs and BV_a equal base value added, the formula becomes:

$$G - (L + E + Vi) = BV_a$$

Base value added per farm for the sample varied from Col $199 to Col $1,170,007. The average base value added per farm in Sevilla was Col $51,342. For Caicedonia the average was Col $147,489. For the entire sample the average base value added per farm was Col $99,415. Base value added for each farm is shown in Table 71.

TABLE 67

Value of Base Output for 50 Farms in
Sevilla and Caicedonia, 1964
(in pesos)

Farm	Coffee	Platano & Yuca	Other	Total
1	50,960	--	32,500	83,460
2	294,000	--	--	294,000
3	84,000	--	--	84,000
4	25,550	--	--	25,550
5	39,400	--	--	39,400
6	16,380	--	--	16,380
7	216,000	--	--	216,000
8	14,000	--	--	14,000
9	13,800	--	9,100	22,900
10	--	--	675,000	675,000
11	35,000	--	27,000	62,000
12	10,500	--	--	10,500
13	55,125	--	--	55,125
14	58,800	20,320	--	79,120
15	10,800	600	--	11,400
16	18,125	480	--	18,605
17	14,400	150	--	14,550
18	21,021	250	--	21,271
19	104,000	6,900	--	110,900
20	24,500	4,464	--	28,964
21	24,500	--	--	24,500
22	49,000	--	--	49,000
23	14,000	--	--	14,000
24	2,700	2,840	3,150	8,690
25	1,470	75	--	1,545

Farm	Coffee	Platano & Yuca	Other	Total
26	63,000	--	--	63,000
27	1,470,000	--	--	1,470,000
28	588,000	2,000	--	590,000
29	210,000	3,500	--	213,500
30	27,100	--	--	27,100
31	28,000	2,400	4,350	34,750
32	3,900	--	540	4,440
33	28,000	--	240	28,240
34	--	--	385,025	385,025
35	43,800	--	1,377,900	1,421,700
36	120,000	--	16,000	136,000
37	10,500	--	--	10,500
38	87,100	4,000	--	91,100
39	70,000	3,600	--	73,600
40	84,700	--	400	85,100
41	52,800	--	--	52,800
42	326,400	--	--	326,400
43	65,250	--	42,460	107,710
44	32,500	--	--	32,500
45	36,400	--	--	36,400
46	22,400	75	--	22,475
47	130,000	3,500	--	133,500
48	102,000	--	--	102,000
49	67,000	3,000	2,880	72,880
50	35,750	--	--	35,750
Total:	4,912,631	58,154	2,576,545	7,547,330

Source: Consumer Survey.

TABLE 68

Value of Total Output per Hectare for 50 Farms
in Sevilla and Caicedonia, 1964

Farm	Total Output (Col $)	Hectares	Output per Hect. (Col $)
1	83,460	4.5	18,547
2	294,000	30.7	9,577
3	84,000	28.8	2,917
4	25,550	11.5	2,222
5	39,400	6.4	6,156
6	16,380	9.6	1,706
7	216,000	64.0	3,375
8	14,000	7.7	1,818
9	22,900	76.8	298
10	675,000	1,280.0	527
11	62,000	71.7	865
12	10,500	6.4	1,641
13	55,125	32.0	1,723
14	79,120	38.4	2,060
15	11,400	9.6	1,188
16	18,605	3.2	5,814
17	14,550	10.2	1,426
18	21,270	12.8	1,662
19	110,900	51.2	2,166
20	28,964	12.8	2,263
21	24,500	10.9	2,248
22	49,000	12.2	4,016
23	14,000	7.7	1,818
24	8,690	4.5	1,931
25	1,545	3.8	403

Farm	Total Output (Col $)	Hectares	Output per Hect. (Col $)
26	63,000	22.4	2,813
27	1,470,000	203.5	7,224
28	590,000	128.0	4,609
29	213,500	76.8	2,780
30	37,100	20.5	1,810
31	34,750	7.7	4,513
32	4,440	2.6	1,708
33	28,240	7.7	3,668
34	385,025	278.4	1,383
35	1,421,700	326.4	4,356
36	136,000	64.0	2,125
37	10,500	7.7	1,364
38	91,100	51.2	1,779
39	73,600	20.5	3,590
40	85,100	19.2	4,432
41	52,800	25.6	2,063
42	326,400	160.0	2,040
43	107,710	28.8	3,740
44	32,500	10.2	3,186
45	36,400	76.8	474
46	22,475	5.1	4,407
47	133,500	25.6	5,215
48	102,000	31.4	3,248
49	72,880	51.2	1,423
50	35,750	10.2	3,505
Total:	7,547,330	3,468.9	2,176

Source: Consumer Survey.

139

TABLE 69

Coffee Yields in Arrobas per Hectare for
50 Farms in Sevilla and Caicedonia, 1964

Farm	Production	Hectares	Yield
1	910	4.5	202
2	4,000	28.2	142
3	1,200	22.4	54
4	350	11.5	30
5	580	6.4	91
6	260	9.6	27
7	3,000	51.2	59
8	200	5.8	34
9	200	9.6	21
10	--	--	--
11	500	10.9	46
12	150	4.5	33
13	750	25.0	30
14	800	19.2	42
15	150	5.1	29
16	250	3.2	78
17	200	7.0	29
18	315	12.8	25
19	1,600	51.2	31
20	350	7.0	50
21	350	10.3	34
22	700	10.9	64
23	200	6.4	31
24	40	2.6	15
25	20	1.9	11

Farm	Production	Hectares	Yield
26	900	19.2	47
27	20,000	192.0	104
28	8,400	127.4	66
29	3,000	64.0	47
30	530	18.6	28
31	400	6.4	63
32	60	2.0	30
33	400	7.1	56
34	--	--	--
35	600	7.7	78
36	2,000	38.4	52
37	150	6.4	23
38	1,300	44.8	29
39	1,000	16.0	63
40	1,210	16.0	76
41	800	22.4	36
42	4,800	140.8	34
43	900	25.0	36
44	500	9.0	56
45	5,200	64.0	81
46	320	5.1	63
47	2,000	25.0	80
48	1,500	28.2	53
49	1,000	50.6	20
50	550	9.0	61
Total:	75,225	1,272.3	59

Source: Consumer Survey.

TABLE 70

Percentage of Farm Output Derived from Various Products
on 50 Farms in Sevilla and Caicedonia, 1964

Farm	Coffee	Platano	Yuca	Poultry	Beef	Milk	Other
1	60	--	--	40	--	--	--
2	100	--	--	--	--	--	--
3	100	--	--	--	--	--	--
4	100	--	--	--	--	--	--
5	100	--	--	--	--	--	--
6	100	--	--	--	--	--	--
7	100	--	--	--	--	--	--
8	100	--	--	--	--	--	--
9	60	--	--	--	--	40	--
10	--	--	--	--	100	--	--
11	56	--	--	--	44	--	--
12	100	--	--	--	--	--	--
13	100	--	--	--	--	--	--
14	74	21	5	--	--	--	--
15	95	5	--	--	--	--	--
16	97	3	--	--	--	--	--
17	98	2	--	--	--	--	--
18	99	1	--	--	--	--	--
19	95	6	--	--	--	--	--
20	85	15	--	--	--	--	--
21	100	--	--	--	--	--	--
22	100	--	--	--	--	--	--
23	100	--	--	--	--	--	--
24	31	3	--	36	--	30	--
25	96	3	1	--	--	--	--

26	100	--	--	--	--	--
27	100	--	--	--	--	--
28	99	1	--	--	--	--
29	98	2	--	--	--	--
30	100	--	--	--	--	--
31	80	7	--	--	--	13
32	88	--	--	--	--	12
33	99	--	--	--	--	1
34	--	--	--	9	--	91
35	3	--	--	4	2	91
36	88	--	--	12	--	--
37	100	--	--	--	--	--
38	96	4	--	--	--	--
39	95	5	--	--	--	--
40	99	--	1	--	--	--
41	100	--	--	--	--	--
42	100	--	--	--	--	--
43	61	--	39	--	--	--
44	100	--	--	--	--	--
45	100	--	--	--	--	--
46	99	1	--	--	--	--
47	97	3	--	--	--	--
48	100	--	--	--	--	--
49	92	4	--	--	--	4
50	100	--	--	--	--	--

Source: Community Survey.

TABLE 71

Base Value Added of 50 Farms in
Sevilla and Caicedonia, 1964
(in pesos)

Farm	Base Output	Base Input	Base Value Added
1	83,460	56,763	26,697
2	294,000	155,709	138,291
3	84,000	70,493	13,507
4	25,550	20,225	5,325
5	39,400	17,733	21,667
6	16,380	14,730	1,650
7	216,000	97,432	118,568
8	14,000	8,268	5,732
9	22,900	3,196	19,704
10	675,000	61,093	613,907
11	62,000	21,465	40,535
12	10,500	6,723	3,777
13	55,125	28,288	26,837
14	79,120	8,103	71,017
15	11,400	2,678	8,722
16	18,605	1,604	17,001
17	14,550	1,474	13,076
18	21,271	18,120	3,151
19	110,900	43,006	67,894
20	28,964	5,504	23,460
21	24,500	21,053	3,447
22	49,000	24,984	24,016
23	14,000	3,921	10,079
24	8,690	3,388	5,302
25	1,545	1,346	199

Farm	Base Output	Base Input	Base Value Added
26	63,000	18,750	44,250
27	1,470,000	460,080	1,009,920
28	590,000	182,546	407,454
29	213,500	99,289	114,211
30	37,100	24,223	12,877
31	34,750	19,248	15,502
32	4,440	3,143	1,297
33	28,240	14,082	14,158
34	385,025	246,096	138,929
35	1,421,700	251,693	1,170,007
36	136,000	75,858	60,142
37	10,500	6,756	3,744
38	91,100	21,558	69,542
39	73,600	27,080	46,520
40	85,100	12,356	72,744
41	52,800	5,460	47,340
42	326,400	125,597	200,803
43	107,710	31,472	76,238
44	32,500	28,554	3,946
45	36,400	29,074	7,326
46	22,475	8,666	13,809
47	133,500	96,968	36,532
48	102,000	15,968	86,032
49	72,880	59,445	13,435
50	35,750	15,283	20,467
Total:	7,547,330	2,576,544	4,970,786

Source: Consumer Survey.

Dividing the base value added per farm by the
number of farm dwellers on each farm gave the base
value added per capita. For family-operated farms
base value added per capita would correspond closely with per capita income. Average value added per
capita for all farm dwellers in Sevilla was Col
$6,864. In Caicedonia it was considerably higher,
Col $23,045. For the entire sample the average
value added per capita was Col $14,325. Value added
per capita for each farm is shown in Table 72.

Dividing the base value added for each farm by
the number of hectares in the farm gave the value
added per hectare. In Sevilla the average value
added per hectare was Col $710. In Caicedonia it
was three times higher, Col $2,219. For the entire
sample the average value added per hectare was approximately one tenth of the value added per capita
or Col $1,433. Value added per hectare for each
farm is shown in Table 73.

Cooperative Knowledge

Respondents were asked how they would describe
a rural electric cooperative. An acceptable answer
was judged as one that explained in very general
terms that a rural electric cooperative is an association of members who have formed an organization
to provide themselves with electric service at the
lowest cost. Out of the 50 respondents only 15
gave acceptable answers.

Of the 25 respondents in Sevilla, 9 replied
with an acceptable description while only 6 of the
25 respondents in Caicedonia gave an acceptable explanation. This difference can be attributed partly to the fact that the rural electric cooperative
office was located only in Sevilla and more informa-
tional meetings were held in the Municipio of Sevilla than Caicedonia. Also, organization problems
in Sevilla caused the cooperative to be discussed
in more detail by the entire population of the
Municipio.

TABLE 72

Value Added per Capita for 50 Farms
in Sevilla and Caicedonia, 1964

Farm	Value Added per Farm (Col $)	No. of Dwellers per Farm	Value Added per Capita (Col $)
1	26,697	5	5,339
2	138,291	5	27,658
3	13,507	10	1,351
4	5,325	12	444
5	21,667	14	1,548
6	1,650	8	206
7	118,568	4	29,642
8	5,732	7	819
9	19,704	9	2,189
10	613,907	4	153,477
11	40,535	10	4,054
12	3,777	2	1,889
13	26,837	8	3,355
14	71,017	6	11,668
15	8,722	5	1,744
16	17,001	9	1,889
17	13,076	14	934
18	3,151	7	450
19	67,894	13	5,223
20	23,460	7	3,351
21	3,447	10	345
22	24,016	9	2,668
23	10,079	1	10,079
24	5,302	6	884
25	199	2	100

(Continued)

TABLE 72 (Continued)

Farm	Value Added per Farm (Col $)	No. of Dwellers per Farm	Value Added per Capita (Col $)
26	44,250	7	6,321
27	1,009,920	6	168,320
28	407,454	4	101,864
29	114,211	4	28,553
30	12,877	9	1,431
31	15,502	9	1,722
32	1,297	2	649
33	14,158	4	3,540
34	138,929	1	138,929
35	1,170,007	4	292,502
36	60,142	6	10,024
37	3,744	11	340
38	69,542	1	69,542
39	46,520	5	9,304
40	72,744	13	5,596
41	47,340	7	6,763
42	200,803	11	18,255
43	76,238	6	12,706
44	3,946	11	359
45	7,326	7	1,047
46	13,809	7	1,973
47	36,532	12	3,044
48	86,032	6	14,339
49	13,435	5	2,687
50	20,467	2	10,234
Total:	4,970,786	347	14,325

Source: Consumer Survey.

148

TABLE 73

Value Added per Hectare for 50 Farms
in Sevilla and Caicedonia, 1964

Farm	Base Value Added (Col $)	No. of Hectares	Value Added per Hectare (Col $)
1	26,697	4.5	5,935
2	138,291	20.7	4,505
3	13,507	22.8	469
4	5,325	11.5	463
5	21,667	6.4	3,385
6	1,650	9.6	172
7	118,568	64.0	1,852
8	5,732	7.7	744
9	19,704	76.8	257
10	613,907	1,280.0	480
11	40,535	71.7	565
12	3,777	6.4	590
13	26,837	32.0	839
14	71,017	38.4	1,849
15	8,722	9.6	909
16	17,001	3.2	5,313
17	13,076	10.2	1,282
18	3,151	12.8	246
19	67,894	51.2	1,326
20	23,460	12.8	1,833
21	3,447	10.9	316
22	24,016	12.2	1,969
23	10,079	7.7	1,309
24	5,302	4.5	1,178
25	199	3.8	52

(Continued)

TABLE 73 (Continued)

Farm	Base Value Added (Col $)	No. of Hectares	Value Added per Hectare (Col $)
26	44,250	22.4	2,020
27	1,009,920	203.5	4,963
28	407,454	128.0	3,183
29	114,211	76.8	1,487
30	12,877	20.5	628
31	15,502	7.7	2,013
32	1,297	2.6	499
33	14,158	7.7	1,839
34	138,929	278.4	499
35	1,170,007	326.4	3,585
36	60,142	64.0	940
37	3,744	7.7	486
38	69,542	51.2	1,358
39	46,520	20.5	2,269
40	72,744	19.2	3,789
41	47,340	25.6	1,849
42	200,803	160.0	1,255
43	76,238	28.8	2,647
44	3,946	10.2	387
45	7,326	76.8	94
46	13,809	5.1	2,708
47	36,532	25.6	1,427
48	86,032	21.4	2,740
49	13,435	51.2	262
50	20,467	10.2	2,007
Total:	4,970,786	3,468.9	1,433

Source: Consumer Survey.

This means that only 30 percent of the rural
population that planned to become members of the
rural electric cooperative had a fairly good idea
of the type of organization they were joining.
Forty-eight percent of the respondents gave what
was classified as unacceptable descriptions. These
descriptions stated in general that the cooperative
was a good thing or that it was a benefit to the
community but did not describe the cooperative. A
typical reply was that the electric cooperative
"debe ser una cosa provechosa para la region y
traera progreso," which simply says that it would
be beneficial for the region and will bring progress.

In Caicedonia a larger number of respondents
attempted to describe the electric cooperative, 21
as compared to 18 in Sevilla. But a greater number
gave unacceptable descriptions, 15 as compared to 9
in Sevilla. Of the 25 respondents in Sevilla, 7
simply said that they did not know how to describe
an electric cooperative. Only 4 in Caicedonia said
that they had no idea or did not know. Response to
the question is shown in Table 74.

TABLE 74

Classification of Answers Describing
a Rural Electric Cooperative, 1965

Answers	No. of Answers		
	Sevilla	Caicedonia	Total
Acceptable	9	6	15
Unacceptable	9	15	24
Do not know	7	4	11
Total:	25	25	50

Source: Consumer Survey.

To test their knowledge of the functioning of a rural electric cooperative, respondents were asked a series of five questions. The questions dealt with normal operating procedures and were not designed to be trick questions. Respondents were asked to reply yes, no or do not know.

The first question asked if the electric cooperative is the property of the government. There was little difference in the response between those interviewed in Sevilla and those questioned in Caicedonia. Less than half of the total population knew that the cooperative is not the property of the government. Forty-four percent said it is not, while 18 percent thought that it is. A large percentage, 38 percent, said they did not know.

The second question asked if the manager is elected by the members of the cooperative. Only one respondent, or 2 percent of the sample, knew he is not. Eighty percent said that the manager is elected by the members and 18 percent said they did not know. Again the sample in Sevilla replied almost exactly as did the sample in Caicedonia. The fact that such a large percentage thought erroneously that the manager is elected by the members rather than being appointed by the Board of Directors can be attributed to the election of the provisional manager. Approximately four months before the survey the members held their first general assembly. One of the things they did at that meeting was to elect a provisional manager. The provisional manager was to serve until the cooperative began operation and then the Board of Directors would select a regular manager. This action may have misled several of the respondents to think that the manager was always elected by the members.

The third question asked if anyone in the community could become a member of the rural electric cooperative. About 75 percent of the sample knew that anyone could become a member. Twelve percent said no and 14 percent said they did not know. Again, there was little difference in the division of the sample between Sevilla and Caicedonia.

The fourth question asked if the cooperative always paid dividends each year to its members. More than half, 56 percent, thought erroneously that the cooperative would pay them dividends each year. The fact is that it probably will be several years before the cooperative will be in a financial position to pay any dividends. Only 14 percent knew correctly that the cooperative would not pay dividends every year. A fairly large percentage, 30 percent, said they did not know.

The fifth and final question concerning cooperative operation asked if each member had one vote. The largest percentage replying to all questions, 86 percent, knew that each member does have one vote. None said no and 14 percent said they did not know. A slightly larger percentage of the respondents in Sevilla replied correctly to this question than did respondents in Caicedonia.

Taking into consideration all five questions and giving one point for each correct answer, the sample scored 110 out of a possible 250. This gave an overall score of 44 percent, or less than half of a perfect score. The combined response was as shown in Table 75.

If all six questions are considered and one third of a point is given to each correct answer, the 50 respondents scored 42 out of a possible 100.

When asked if they knew where the money was coming from to build the electric distribution system, almost half of those interviewed replied correctly. Of the respondents, 13, or 26 percent, said the United States, while 16 percent said the Alliance for Progress. To almost everyone, including government officials, the Alliance for Progress and the United States are synonymous. Therefore, combining replies for the Alliance and the United States gives a correct response of 42 percent. Correct replies were equally divided between respondents in Sevilla and Caicedonia.

TABLE 75

Knowledge of Functions of an Electric
Cooperative by 50 Respondents, 1965

Question	No. of Answers		
	True	False	Do Not Know
1. Cooperative is property of government.	9	(22)*	19
2. Manager is elected by members.	40	(01)	9
3. Anyone can be a member.	(37)	6	7
4. Cooperative always pays annual dividends.	28	(07)	15
5. Each member has one vote.	(43)	--	7

*Correct answers are in parentheses.

Source: Consumer Survey.

Two respondents in Sevilla and three in Caicedonia thought the members were providing the money
for the system. In a sense this is true, because
the cooperative, through its members, will repay
the loan to the Colombian Government which will in
turn repay the United States. (See Table 76 for
responses to question of where the money was coming
from.)

Seven of the respondents gave such answers as
a bank, CVC, the Coffee Federation or the Colombian
Government. Seventeen simply said they did not
know where the money was coming from. Thus, almost
half of the respondents, 48 percent, definitely did
not know where the money was coming from to build
the rural electric system. Those who did not know
were scattered throughout both municipios.

TABLE 76

Respondents' Opinions of Source of Funds
to Construct the Rural Electric
Cooperative, 1965

| | No. of Respondents | | |
Source of Funds	Sevilla	Caicedonia	Total
United States	8	5	13
Alliance for Progress	3	5	8
Members	2	3	5
Other source	5	2	7
Do not know	7	10	17
Total:	25	25	50

Source: Consumer Survey.

When considering all seven questions concerning knowledge of the functions and operation of the
rural electric cooperative, the respondents scored
42 out of a possible 100. The scores for each of
the questions separately was very near the score
for all questions combined. Therefore, it seems
rather conclusive that the respondents did not have
a good knowledge of the operation of their future
rural electric cooperative.

The six schoolteachers interviewed were asked
the same questions concerning cooperatives. Only
one of the six teachers gave an acceptable defini-
tion of an electric cooperative. When asked if the
electric cooperative is the property of the government, one said yes, three said no and one said she
did not know.

Five of the teachers thought the manager was
elected by the membership and one did not know.

All teachers thought anyone in the community could
be a member of the cooperative. Four thought the
cooperative always paid dividends and two said it
did not. All six said each member had one vote.

When asked if they knew the source of capital
to construct the electric cooperative, one said the
United States, one said the Alliance for Progress,
three said the members and one said she did not
know.

Thus, awarding 2.4 points for each correct
answer gave a total score of 48 out of 100 for the
teachers. This compared with a score of 42 for the
50 farmers interviewed.

Values and Attitudes

In an effort to establish a bench mark of values respondents were asked two questions concerning
their goals for their children and for themselves.
To establish a bench mark of attitudes they were
asked questions concerning their opinions toward
national and local governments, the local school,
their neighbors and the community.

Respondents were asked what they would like
their son to grow up to be. Response to the question is shown in Table 77. In a few cases where
the respondent did not have a son, the respondent
was told to assume that he had a son. The most
popular choice was for the son to grow up to be a
doctor, while the next highest number said an agri-
culturalist. This included such professions as
agronomist and agricultural engineer.

Respondents were asked what their goal or am-
bition was in life. Answers to this question are
shown in Table 78. The highest percentage, 34 percent, said it was to improve their level of living.
Another fairly large group, 20 percent, said it was
to work. This can be interpreted to mean that they
wanted to be able to maintain their health and have
the opportunity to continue working as they had been.

TABLE 77

Choice of Professions for Children by 50 Respondents in Sevilla and Caicedonia, 1965

Profession	No. of Respondents		
	Sevilla	Caicedonia	Total
Doctor	3	8	11
Agriculturalist	5	3	8
Engineer	3	4	7
Lawyer	2	2	4
Priest	1	2	3
Mechanic	2	1	3
Businessman	1	1	2
Pilot	1	1	2
Chauffeur	1	-	1
Schoolteacher	1	-	1
Read and write	-	1	1
What he chooses	2	1	3
Do not know	3	1	4
Total:	25	25	50

Source: Consumer Survey.

TABLE 78

Goals in Life of 50 Respondents in Sevilla and Caicedonia, 1965

Goal	No. of Respondents		
	Sevilla	Caicedonia	Total
Improve level of living	11	6	17
To work	3	7	10
Educate children	5	4	9
Make money	1	3	4
Buy own farm	-	3	3
Own a business	1	-	1
Be a good citizen	1	-	1
Live in a city	2	-	2
Take a vacation	-	1	1
Do not know	1	1	2
Total:	25	25	50

Source: Consumer Survey.

Eighteen percent of the respondents said they wanted
to educate their children and 8 percent said they
wanted to make money. Sixteen percent gave other
goals, such as to own a business, buy a house in
Sevilla, live in a city, be a good citizen or take
a vacation. Seven percent said they wanted to buy
their own farm.

Respondents in Caicedonia had a more favorable
attitude toward the accomplishments of national and
municipal governments than did those respondents in
Sevilla. Attitudes toward the local school were
quite similar as were the attitudes toward neighbors
and living conditions in the community. These attitudes and opinions are recorded in Table 79. The
combined response of Sevilla and Caicedonia showed
the least favorable attitude toward the work of the
municipal government, only slightly better for the
national government, somewhat better for operation
of the local school, a perfect attitude toward their
neighbors and almost a completely positive attitude
toward improvement of living conditions in the community.

TABLE 79

Attitudes of 50 Respondents in Sevilla
and Caicedonia toward Government,
School and Community, 1965

Question	No. of Respondents		
	Yes	No	Do Not Know
National government has done a good job.	36	3	11
Municipio government has done a good job.	35	6	9
Local school is managed well.	40	7	3
Neighbors are helpful and cooperative.	50	-	-
Living conditions have improved.	49	1	-

Source: Consumer Survey.

Respondents were asked if they thought the
national government had done a good job during the
past three years. Of the 25 respondents in Sevilla,
16 thought it had, 2 said no and 7 said they did not
know. It seemed apparent that some of the respondents who said they did not know actually thought
no, but preferred to be noncommittal. In Caicedonia 20 respondents thought the national government had done a good job, while only 1 said no and
4 said they did not know.

The negative opinions were that the government
simply was not capable, that there were no loans
for small industry and that the government had not
done anything to help the farmer.

Attitude toward the work of the municipal government was slightly more negative, 12 percent as
compared to 6 percent for the national government.
Of the respondents, 70 percent thought the municipal
governments had done a good job during the past
three years. Only one respondent in Caicedonia
thought the municipal government had not done a
good job. This respondent said the military mayor
of Caicedonia did not understand the problems of
the rural areas.

In Sevilla fewer respondents, 16, thought the
municipal government had done a good job and more,
5, thought it had not done a good job. The 5 negative viewpoints said there was too much politics
involved, that it lacked money and that it did not
do anything in the rural villages. Almost 20 percent of the total sample was noncommittal.

Most of the negative attitude toward work of
the municipal government was expressed by those respondents living north of Sevilla. These respondents seemed quite anxious for electric service and
understood the problem of the municipal government
delaying operation of the electric cooperative.
Thus, this action may have caused their attitude
to be somewhat hostile to the municipal government.

Only three respondents were noncommittal about
management of the local school. Consequently, more
respondents expressed both positive and negative
attitudes for the local school than they did for
national and municipal governments. Eighty percent
said the local schools had been managed well during
the past three years. Four respondents in Sevilla
and three in Caicedonia said they had not. Their
reasons were that there was poor instruction, that
there were no aids for instruction, that the teacher
lived in Sevilla and was too far away, that there
was little interest in the school, that the school
had a bad location and that the teacher had low
morals.

When asked if their neighbors had been helpful
and cooperative during the past three years, all of
the respondents in both municipios said yes. Most
respondents made a point to express how helpful
their neighbors had been and there did not seem to
be anyone who did not like or get along well with
his neighbors.

The fifth question was designed to determine
the attitude of respondents toward living conditions
in their community. They were asked if living conditions had improved during the past three years.
All the respondents except one said yes. The negative attitude was expressed by a young, progressive
farmer who had expressed the view that the military
mayor did not understand the problems of the rural
areas. He said conditions in the community had remained the same during the past three years.

Almost all respondents cited the end of the
violence as the reason for better living conditions
in the community. Some said there was more peace,
some said more tranquility, some said the army in
the region had improved conditions and some said
there was more security. One respondent said the
attitude of the people had improved, another said
there was better transportation, another cited a
new aqueduct and another a new school. However,
one older farmer who said conditions had improved

because the army had brought peace to the region
also said that Sevilla was dying. He had lived in
the Sevilla area for 50 years but planned to sell
his farm and move to Cali.

If conditions in the area were perfect and all
interviewed had expressed positive attitudes toward
national government, local government, school, neighbors and community there would have been a total of
250 points for each positive attitude. Transferring
the scoring system to the basis of 100 results in a
score of 84. Thus, the survey showed that 84 percent of the sample had positive attitudes toward
government, school and community.

Rating the most positive attitudes first shows
that the sample thought the most of their neighbors,
next the community, then the school, the national
government and that they had the least respect for
the municipal government.

The six schoolteachers were also asked the same
questions concerning values and attitudes. Two
teachers wanted their sons to grow up to be doctors,
two wanted their sons to be lawyers, one wanted him
to be an electrical engineer and the sixth teacher
wanted her son to attend a university and not be a
laborer.

Their own goals in life were varied. One said
she wanted to achieve greater things, one wanted to
have good health and help others to learn, one
wanted her children to have a professional career,
one wanted to study, specializing in languages, another wanted to teach and the sixth wanted to travel.

When asked if the national government was doing
a good job, all said yes. All thought the municipal
government was also doing a good job. All said the
local school was being run properly and that the
neighbors were cooperative.

All but one of the teachers thought conditions
in the local area had improved during the past three

years. The exception thought conditions were about
the same. All of the five teachers who thought conditions had improved cited suppression of the violence as the reason. One teacher also said a new
road had been built and an aqueduct installed.

Considering attitude toward government, school,
neighbors, and community, the teachers had a near
perfect attitude of 97 percent. This compared with
84 percent for the survey of 50 farmers.

Appliance Sales

There were six stores in the project area selling electric appliances at the time of the survey
in March, 1965. Four stores were located in Sevilla,
two were in Caicedonia. Both of the stores in Caicedonia reported their sales for 1963 and 1964, but
only two of the four stores in Sevilla were willing
to release this information. It was estimated that
sales of the two stores in Sevilla not reporting
were approximately equal to the sales of the two
stores that did report.

Sales of electric appliances in Caicedonia
were relatively small compared to those in Sevilla.
Light bulbs, irons and radios were the most numerous items sold. Television sets, however, accounted
for the highest value of items sold. In 1964 it was
estimated that television sets accounted for 43 percent of the sales value of all electric appliances
in Sevilla and Caicedonia, while incandescent bulbs
and fluorescent tubes accounted for 25 percent.
The remaining sales consisted of electric irons,
radios, blenders and heat lamps. There were some
purchases of electric motors and other appliances
from larger cities outside the cooperative area.
These purchases were small and no estimates of the
number of items or value were made.

Sales of electrical appliances in 1963 and
1964 among the four stores reporting in Sevilla and
Caicedonia were as shown in Tables 80 and 81. Average prices for the items sold in 1964 were as shown
in Table 82.

TABLE 80

Sales of Electrical Appliances among Four
Stores in Sevilla and Caicedonia, 1963

| Item | No. of Sales According to Store No. & Location | | | |
	(1) Sevilla	(2) Sevilla	(3) Caicedonia	(4) Caicedonia
Light bulbs	2,000	1,500	500	--
Fluorescent tubes	250	408	--	20
Irons	100	36	36	30
Radios	30	12	--	35
Heat lamps	6	--	--	8
Televisions	3	1	--	1
Blenders	5	--	--	--

Source: Appliance Sales Survey.

TABLE 81

Sales of Electrical Appliances among Four
Stores in Sevilla and Caicedonia, 1964

| Item | No. of Sales According to Store No. & Location | | | |
	(1) Sevilla	(2) Sevilla	(3) Caicedonia	(4) Caicedonia
Light bulbs	3,000	2,150	800	--
Fluorescent tubes	350	408	--	30
Irons	150	54	44	25
Radios	30	12	--	35
Heat lamps	6	--	--	8
Televisions	3	1	--	1
Blenders	5	--	--	--

Source: Appliance Sales Survey.

TABLE 82

Average Prices of Electrical Appliances
in Sevilla and Caicedonia, 1964
(in pesos)

| | Prices According to Store No. & Location | | | |
| | (1) | (2) | (3) | (4) |
Item	Sevilla	Sevilla	Caice-donia	Caice-donia
Light bulbs	3.0	3.75	2.50	--
Fluorescent tubes	10.0	13.50	--	10.50
Irons	50.0	61.05	48.0	57.80
Radios	350.0	350.0	--	515.0
Heat lamps	150.0	--	--	195.0
Blenders	400.0	465.0	--	--
Televisions	3,900.0	3,975.0	--	3,975.0

Source: Appliance Sales Survey.

One store owner in Caicedonia observed that
sales of electric applicances in the area were
scarce because it was much easier for the people in
Caicedonia to purchase appliances on time in Armenia.
He also said electric stoves were not sold in the
area because the cost of energy was too high.

An estimate of sales of electric appliances in
the project area was made for 1963 and 1964 using
1964 average prices. The sales of the two stores in
Sevilla not reporting was assumed to be equal to
those reporting. The estimated annual value of appliance sales value in 1963 and 1964 were as shown
in Tables 83 and 84.

TABLE 83

Estimated Annual Value of Appliance Sales
in Sevilla and Caicedonia, 1963
(in pesos)

Item	No. of Sales	Average Price	Total Value
Light bulbs	7,500	3.0	22,500
Fluorescent tubes	1,336	13.50	18,036
Irons	338	60.0	20,280
Radios	119	350.0	41,650
Heat lamps	20	150.0	3,000
Blenders	10	400.0	4,000
Televisions	9	3,975.0	35,775
Total:			145,241

Source: Appliance Sales Survey.

TABLE 84

Estimated Annual Value of Appliance Sales
in Sevilla and Caicedonia, 1964
(in pesos)

Item	No. of Sales	Average Price	Total Value
Light bulbs	11,100	3.0	33,300
Fluorescent tubes	1,546	13.50	20,871
Irons	477	60.0	28,620
Radios	182	350.0	63,700
Heat lamps	25	150.0	3,750
Blenders	22	400.0	8,800
Televisions	23	3,975.0	91,425
Total:			250,466

Source: Appliance Sales Survey.

PROJECTION OF DEVELOPMENT VALUE

Farm inputs and outputs were projected on the basis of stated production plans after the availability of electricity. For purposes of projection it was assumed that each farmer planning to change his production plans would do so in accordance with his intentions. In cases where farmers had stated they would change production but were vague in their plans, projected production was left unchanged from 1964. Therefore, on these farms rural electrification was not given credit for stimulating changes in production plans.

Labor and variable inputs were projected in relation to the planned changes in output. Energy inputs were computed on the basis of the intended uses of electricity. Projected labor, energy and variable inputs after the availability of electricity were then subtracted from the projected outputs. The result was projected value added to the national economy for the 50 farms surveyed.

To obtain the development value of rural electrification, the base value added was subtracted from the projected value added.

Production Plans

Respondents were asked if they intended to change their production plans within three years after electricity became available. Response to the question is shown in Table 85. Sixty-two percent said they would change production plans, 24 percent said they would not and 14 percent said they did not know.

A slightly larger number of respondents in Sevilla said they would change production plans than did respondents in Caicedonia. Also, a slightly larger number said they would not change production plans after electricity became available. A larger number in Caicedonia were undecided about their production plans and said they did not know if they would change.

TABLE 85

Intended Changes in Production Plans with
Availability of Electricity on 50 Farms
in Sevilla and Caicedonia

Change in Plans	No. of Respondents		
	Sevilla	Caicedonia	Total
Intending to change	17	14	31
Not intending to change	7	5	12
Undecided	1	6	7
Total:	25	25	50

Source: Consumer Survey.

Of those operations that respondents were intending to expand, coffee was mentioned most frequently (see Table 86). However, there were more
respondents planning to start new poultry operations
than there were planning to expand coffee production. Three other respondents already producing
poultry were planning to expand production after
electricity became available. Poultry production
is an enterprise that lends itself to the use of
electricity and this combined with a favorable market for poultry undoubtedly was responsible for the
intended changes in production plans.

New production also was being planned by some
respondents for milk and pork. One respondent who
operated a small canteen, or beverage store, in connection with his farm enterprise said he expected
to expand the size of his store because it paid
more than his farm. Another respondent who operated a larger general store as well as his farm
planned to open a movie theater after electricity
became available in the small rural village.

TABLE 86

Number of Respondents Intending to Expand
or Add New Enterprises within Three Years
after the Availability of Electricity

Enterprise	Sevilla		Caicedonia	
	Expand	Add New	Expand	Add New
Coffee	8	--	3	--
Poultry	2	9	1	8
Dairy	2	2	--	1
Swine	1	4	1	--
Sugar cane	--	--	1	--
Platano	1	--	1	--
Cocoa	--	--	1	--
Beef	--	--	1	--
Yuca	1	--	--	--
Canteen	1	--	--	--
Movie theater	--	1	--	--
Starch plant	--	2	--	--

Source: Consumer Survey.

Two farmers in Sevilla who were producing yuca
said they wanted to start an industry to obtain
starch from yuca. The starch would be used in laun-
dering clothes and in making bread and other products.

The total number of respondents in the cooperative area planning to expand or start new enterprises and the total planning to increase production within three years after electricity became
available were as shown in Table 87.

Projected Energy Consumption

On the basis of the intended uses of electricity within three years after it became available,

the projected value of energy consumed was computed.
There was no attempt to differentiate between productive and consumptive uses of electricity. Energy
costs were computed for all uses of electricity.

Most of the farmers expected to replace the
gasoline engines they had with electric motors. In
some cases farmers intended to replace hand labor
with electric motors. In addition to the costs of
operating electric motors, energy costs were also
computed for all electric appliances that the respondent intended to purchase within three years.
Therefore, projected energy costs were computed almost entirely as costs of consumption of electric
energy.

TABLE 87

Total Number of Respondents Planning
to Increase Production after the
Availability of Electricity

	No. of Respondents		
Enterprise	Expand	Add New	Total
Coffee	11	--	11
Poultry	3	17	20
Dairy	2	3	5
Swine	2	4	6
Sugar cane	1	--	1
Platano	2	--	2
Cocoa	1	--	1
Beef	1	--	1
Yuca	1	--	1
Canteen	1	--	1
Movie theater	--	1	1
Starch plant	--	2	2

Source: Consumer Survey.

Average annual kilowatt-hour consumption was determined for each type of appliance and the different size electric motors. Consumption figures were based on studies made in the United States and by the United Nations. These figures were then modified in consultation with CVC electrical engineers and other persons familiar with the area. Annual average kilowatt-hour (KWH) consumption for various appliances is shown in Table 88.

Cost of electric energy consumption was then based on monthly kilowatt-hour consumption for each respondent. Retail rates as proposed in the cooperative's loan application were used to determine the monthly and annual value of electric energy consumption.

The cost of electricity was computed on the basis of Col $6.00 for the first 20 KWH or less consumed each month. The second step was based on Col $0.26 for each KWH thereafter up to and including 100 KWH. All KWH's consumed each month over 100 KWH were based on Col $0.24 per KWH.

All except 2 of the 25 farms in Sevilla were planning to purchase electric motors. The 2 farms not intending to purchase electric motors had relatively small operations and human energy was the sole source of power.

In Caicedonia 7 of the 25 farms were not planning to purchase electric motors. Of the 7 farms, 6 were using gasoline engines to dispulp coffee and they planned to continue using these engines rather than purchasing electric motors. The other 2 farms planned to continue using hand labor to dispulp coffee.

The annual and monthly kilowatt-hour consumption and monthly electric cost for the 50 farms in Sevilla and Caicedonia were projected as shown in Table 89.

TABLE 88

Annual Average Kilowatt-Hour Consumption of Various Electrical Items

Electrical Item	Annual Average Kilowatt-Hour Usage
Incandescent bulb for house lighting	55
Fluorescent tube for house lighting	20
Radio	100
Fan	75
Television	300
Air conditioner	1,500
Tape recorder	50
Blender	30
Range	1,200
Record player	50
Burglar alarm	50
Sewing machine	25
Incandescent bulb for utility lighting	20
Infrared-type poultry brooder	1 per bird
Iron	80
Refrigerator	360
Washing machine	60
Incubator	1 per five eggs
Night lighting, 100 birds	1,200
Milk cooler 1/4-5 HP	12 per 100 gals.
Milker, portable 1/4-1/2 HP	18 per cow
Corn, ear shelling 1/4-5 HP	7 per 100 bu.
Feed grinding, 1-10 HP	1 per 200 lbs.
Food freezer	1,000
Water pump, shallow well	100
Water pump, deep well	200
Electric motors:	
1/2 HP and less	150
2/3-3/4 HP	175
1-1 3/4 HP	200
2-3 HP	250
4-5 HP	300
6-7 HP	500
8-9 HP	1,000
10 HP and over	1,000 per HP

Source: Based on U.S. and U.N. studies and on consultations with Latin American electrical engineers.

TABLE 89

Projected Annual and Monthly Consumption
and Cost of Electric Energy on 50 Farms
in Sevilla and Caicedonia

Farm	Annual KWH Consumption	Monthly KWH Consumption	Monthly Cost (Col $)	Annual Cost (Col $)
1	3,289	274	68.56	823
2	3,165	264	66.20	794
3	1,565	130	34.00	408
4	3,370	281	70.20	842
5	660	55	15.10	181
6	285	24	7.04	84
7	2,180	182	46.48	558
8	1,365	114	30.16	362
9	1,695	141	36.64	440
10	2,590	216	54.64	656
11	1,290	108	28.72	345
12	1,755	146	37.84	454
13	2,580	115	30.40	365
14	1,640	137	35.68	428
15	685	57	15.62	187
16	1,155	96	25.76	309
17	1,420	118	31.12	373
18	1,980	165	42.40	509
19	2,325	177	45.28	543
20	1,330	111	29.44	353
21	1,480	123	32.32	388
22	1,715	143	37.12	445
23	345	29	8.34	100
24	975	81	21.86	262
25	345	29	8.34	100

Farm	Annual KWH Consumption	Monthly KWH Consumption	Monthly Cost (Col $)	Annual Cost (Col $)
26	1,290	108	28.72	345
27	7,060	588	143.92	1,727
28	740	62	16.92	203
29	2,065	172	44.08	529
30	1,705	142	36.88	443
31	2,395	200	50.80	610
32	400	33	9.38	113
33	540	45	12.50	150
34	59,800	4,983	1,198.72	14,375
35	57,245	4,770	1,147.60	13,771
36	2,050	171	43.84	526
37	850	71	19.26	231
38	1,300	108	28.72	345
39	605	50	13.80	166
40	815	68	18.48	222
41	1,100	92	24.72	297
42	2,580	215	54.50	653
43	1,985	165	42.40	509
44	1,115	93	24.98	300
45	2,295	191	48.64	584
46	1,000	83	22.38	269
47	4,190	349	86.56	1,039
48	820	68	22.48	270
49	1,040	87	20.82	250
50	265	22	6.52	78
Average	3,929	325	80.54	966

Source: Consumer Survey.

Some other farms planned to continue purchasing fuel for various uses. Two large sugar cane farms would need fuel for tractor power, while one large coffee farm would need fuel to operate the coffee drier. Cost of fuels was added to the cost of electric energy to obtain total projected energy costs.

A comparison of base energy costs with projected energy costs showed that for Sevilla energy costs would be increased for 15 farms and reduced for 10 farms. Additional energy costs for the 25 farms were projected at Col $963. The comparison of base and projected costs in Sevilla was as shown in Table 90.

Projected energy costs for Caicedonia showed that 11 farms would have added costs while 14 farms would reduce costs. Additional energy costs for the 25 farms in Caicedonia were projected at Col $1,248.

Projected Input

Inputs for each of the 50 farms were projected on the basis of production plans. No allowances were made for technological innovations that might reduce the amount of input per unit of output. It was assumed that one unit of base input would be required to produce one unit of projected output. The only change in inputs was in the substitution of electric energy costs for the costs of fuels.

Variable inputs, such as for feed, seed, fertilizer and pesticide were projected on the basis of inputs in 1964. That is, where one unit of fertilizer was used to produce one unit of coffee in the base period, the same ratio was applied for projected inputs.

The projected value of labor, energy and variable inputs for the sample of 50 farms in Sevilla and Caicedonia are shown in Table 91. Total projected inputs varied in value from Col $1,300 to Col $319,838. Value of projected inputs were substantially higher in Caicedonia than in Sevilla.

TABLE 90

Comparison of Base Energy Costs with Projected Energy
Costs for 50 Farms in Sevilla and Caicedonia
(in pesos)

Farm	Base Energy Costs	Projected Energy Costs	Added Cost	Reduced Cost
1	127	823	696	--
2	309	794	485	--
3	293	408	115	--
4	845	842	--	3
5	153	181	28	--
6	90	84	--	6
7	832	558	--	274
8	548	362	--	186
9	156	440	284	--
10	773	656	--	117
11	825	345	--	480
12	823	454	--	369
13	358	365	7	--
14	603	428	--	175
15	128	187	59	--
16	104	309	205	--
17	244	373	129	--
18	120	509	389	--
19	766	543	--	223
20	104	353	249	--
21	303	388	85	--
22	444	445	1	--
23	96	100	4	--
24	156	262	106	--
25	146	100	--	46

(Continued)

TABLE 90 (Continued)

Farm	Base Energy Costs	Projected Energy Costs	Added Cost	Reduced Cost
26	420	345	--	75
27	10,800	12,527	1,727	--
28	426	389	--	37
29	3,789	529	--	3,260
30	423	443	20	--
31	834	610	--	224
32	144	113	--	31
33	132	186	54	--
34	46,696	39,375	--	7,321
35	26,623	38,771	12,148	--
36	858	526	--	332
37	656	527	--	129
38	78	345	267	--
39	320	166	--	154
40	236	222	--	14
41	247	297	50	--
42	1,797	653	--	1,144
43	1,092	605	--	487
44	154	300	146	--
45	234	584	350	--
46	166	269	103	--
47	856	1,039	183	--
48	575	270	--	305
49	375	250	--	125
50	283	253	--	30
Total	107,560	109,903	2,343	--

Source: Consumer Survey.

TABLE 91

Projected Value of Labor, Energy and Variable
Inputs for 50 Farms in Sevilla and Caicedonia
(in pesos)

Farm	Labor Input	Energy Input	Variable Input	Total Input
1	51,102	823	15,030	66,955
2	150,228	794	16,050	167,072
3	89,856	408	--	90,264
4	20,592	842	3,228	24,662
5	23,040	181	5,088	28,309
6	14,400	84	240	14,724
7	90,000	558	6,600	97,158
8	5,440	362	2,280	8,082
9	10,400	440	10,585	21,425
10	49,920	656	10,400	60,976
11	21,360	345	--	21,705
12	3,600	454	2,300	6,354
13	33,930	365	3,000	27,295
14	7,500	428	--	7,928
15	2,550	187	--	2,737
16	5,100	309	3,000	8,409
17	6,675	373	15,255	22,303
18	20,000	509	5,400	25,909
19	49,440	543	35,000	84,983
20	7,400	353	700	8,453
21	18,000	388	2,750	21,138
22	25,040	445	3,000	28,485
23	3,000	100	825	3,925
24	1,200	262	2,242	3,704
25	1,200	100	--	1,300

(Continued)

TABLE 91 (Continued)

Farm	Labor Input	Energy Input	Variable Input	Total Input
26	16,110	345	3,920	20,375
27	449,280	12,527	--	461,807
28	180,000	389	2,120	182,509
29	90,000	529	7,600	98,129
30	21,600	443	6,400	28,443
31	15,964	610	5,950	22,524
32	2,880	113	119	3,112
33	12,960	186	990	14,136
34	162,000	39,375	37,400	238,775
35	242,625	38,771	38,442	319,838
36	75,000	526	--	75,526
37	2,250	527	7,350	10,127
38	20,520	345	960	21,825
39	20,160	166	6,600	26,926
40	11,200	222	920	12,342
41	4,320	297	1,593	6,210
42	121,600	653	2,200	124,453
43	4,000	605	34,980	39,585
44	27,200	300	1,200	28,700
45	14,400	584	14,440	29,424
46	11,000	269	2,600	13,869
47	86,400	1,039	15,700	103,139
48	12,600	270	2,793	15,663
49	56,320	250	2,750	59,320
50	15,000	253	--	15,253
Total:	2,386,362	109,903	340,000	2,836,265

Source: Consumer Survey.

Comparison of the base period inputs with projected inputs showed that 18 of the 25 farms in Sevilla would have additional input costs. Of the 25
farms in Caicedonia, 14 would have additional input
costs. Eleven of the farms in Caicedonia would reduce input costs with the availability of electricity, but only 7 in Sevilla would reduce costs.
Farms having added or reduced input costs based on
a comparison of the value of base inputs with projected inputs are shown in Table 92.

Projected Output

Output was projected on the basis of the intended changes in production plans. Only for those
farms where the operator had specific plans was the
output changed. For the farms that did not have intentions of changing production after electricity
became available, production was projected to be
the same as production had been for 1964. The same
production figures were used also for those farms
that were undecided about changing production or
that had only vague plans.

The value of projected output was obtained by
using projected production and the 1964 market
prices. Comparison of the value of 1964 output
with projected output for the 50 farms is shown in
Table 93. Fifteen of the farms in Sevilla would
have added output with the availability of electricity, while 10 farms in Caicedonia would increase
output. Thus, one out of every two farms sampled
would increase output after electricity became
available.

One of the prominent factors in the projected
output was the increase in the diversification of
products to be marketed. The number of farm products marketed in the base period and the number to
be marketed within three years after the availability are shown in Table 94. While 10 farms in Sevilla indicated they would diversify production,
only 8 in Caicedonia planned to market more products.
The 10 farms in Sevilla planned to market 16 additional products and the 8 farms in Caicedonia planned
to market 11 additional products.

TABLE 92

Comparison of Base Period and Projected Inputs
for 50 Farms in Sevilla and Caicedonia
(in pesos)

Farm	Base Input	Projected Input	Added Input	Reduced Input
1	56,763	66,955	10,192	--
2	155,709	167,072	11,363	--
3	70,493	90,264	19,771	--
4	20,225	24,662	4,437	--
5	17,733	28,309	10,576	--
6	14,730	14,724	--	6
7	97,432	97,158	--	274
8	8,268	8,082	--	186
9	3,196	21,425	18,229	--
10	61,093	60,976	--	117
11	21,465	21,705	240	--
12	6,723	6,354	--	369
13	28,288	37,295	9,007	--
14	8,103	7,928	--	175
15	2,678	2,737	59	--
16	1,604	8,409	6,805	--
17	1,474	22,303	20,829	--
18	18,120	25,909	7,789	--
19	43,006	84,983	41,977	--
20	5,504	8,453	2,949	--
21	21,053	21,138	85	--
22	24,984	28,485	3,501	--
23	3,921	3,925	4	--
24	3,388	3,704	316	--
25	1,346	1,300	--	46

Farm	Base Input	Projected Input	Added Input	Reduced Input
26	18,750	20,375	1,625	--
27	460,080	461,807	1,727	--
28	182,546	182,509	--	37
29	99,289	98,129	--	1,160
30	24,223	29,443	4,220	--
31	19,248	22,524	3,276	--
32	3,043	3,112	--	31
33	14,082	14,136	54	--
34	246,096	238,775	--	7,321
35	251,693	319,838	68,145	--
36	75,858	75,526	--	332
37	6,756	10,127	3,371	--
38	21,558	21,825	267	--
39	27,080	26,926	--	154
40	12,356	12,342	--	14
41	5,460	6,210	750	--
42	125,597	124,453	--	1,144
43	31,472	39,585	8,113	--
44	28,554	28,700	146	--
45	29,074	29,424	350	--
46	8,666	13,869	5,203	--
47	96,968	103,139	6,171	--
48	15,968	15,663	--	305
49	59,445	59,320	--	125
50	15,283	15,253	--	30
Total:	2,576,544	2,836,265	259,721	--

Source: Consumer Survey.

TABLE 93

Comparison of Value of Base Output with Projected
Output for 50 Farms in Sevilla and Caicedonia
(in pesos)

Farm	Base Output	Projected Output	Added Output
1	83,460	108,867	25,407
2	294,000	314,066	20,066
3	84,000	105,800	21,800
4	25,550	30,985	5,435
5	39,400	63,104	23,704
6	16,380	16,380	--
7	216,000	216,000	--
8	14,000	14,000	--
9	22,900	47,585	24,685
10	675,000	675,000	--
11	62,000	65,500	3,500
12	10,500	10,500	--
13	55,125	77,000	21,875
14	79,120	29,120	--
15	11,400	11,400	--
16	18,605	29,705	11,100
17	14,550	38,550	24,000
18	21,271	29,911	8,640
19	110,900	158,900	48,000
20	28,964	31,924	2,960
21	24,500	24,500	--
22	49,000	54,840	5,840
23	14,000	14,000	--
24	8,690	9,328	638
25	1,545	1,545	--

Farm	Base Output	Projected Output	Added Output
26	63,000	67,320	4,320
27	1,470,000	1,470,000	--
28	590,000	590,000	--
29	213,500	216,380	2,880
30	37,100	42,860	5,760
31	34,750	39,550	4,800
32	4,440	4,440	--
33	28,240	28,240	--
34	385,025	385,025	--
35	1,421,700	1,886,250	464,550
36	136,000	136,000	--
37	10,500	15,300	4,800
38	91,100	91,100	--
39	73,600	73,600	--
40	85,100	85,100	--
41	52,800	53,760	960
42	326,400	326,400	--
43	107,710	124,990	17,280
44	32,500	32,500	--
45	36,400	36,400	--
46	22,475	31,305	8,830
47	133,500	142,260	8,760
48	102,000	102,000	--
49	73,880	73,880	--
50	35,750	35,750	--
Total:	7,547,330	8,317,920	770,590

Source: Consumer Survey.

TABLE 94

Projected Diversification of Production
after the Availability of Electricity on
50 Farms in Sevilla and Caicedonia

Farm	Base No. of Products Marketed	Projected No. of Products to be Marketed	Additional No. of Products
1	3	3	-
2	1	1	-
3	1	1	-
4	1	2	1
5	1	1	-
6	1	1	-
7	1	1	-
8	1	1	-
9	2	3	1
10	1	1	-
11	2	2	-
12	1	1	-
13	1	4	3
14	3	2	-
15	2	2	-
16	2	4	2
17	2	3	2
18	2	4	2
19	2	3	1
20	2	4	2
21	1	1	-
22	1	3	2
23	1	1	-
24	4	5	1
25	3	3	-

Farm	Base No. of Products Marketed	Projected No. of Products to be Marketed	Additional No. of Products
26	1	3	2
27	1	1	-
28	2	2	-
29	2	3	1
30	1	2	1
31	3	4	1
32	2	2	-
33	2	2	-
34	2	2	-
35	4	4	-
36	2	2	-
37	1	2	1
38	2	2	-
39	2	2	-
40	2	2	-
41	1	2	1
42	1	1	-
43	3	3	-
44	1	1	-
45	1	1	-
46	2	4	2
47	2	4	2
48	1	1	-
49	3	3	-
50	1	1	-
Total:	87	113	28

Source: Consumer Survey.

185

In 1964 the 50 farms surveyed marketed an average 1.75 product per farm. According to projected
production plans, the 50 farms would diversify to
the extent they would market an average of 2.33
products per farm.

The greatest increase in the value of projected
farm production was for poultry, primarily broilers.
Egg production also would increase substantially according to plans. The percentage increase in production of coffee was relatively small, while that
for livestock and livestock products was much higher.
The value of production marketed in 1964 and the
projected value for the 50 farms, including the value and percentage increase for various commodities,
are shown in Table 95.

TABLE 95

Increased Value of Projected Output Compared
with Base Output for Various Products
(in pesos)

Product	Base Period Output	Projected Output	Value Increase	Percent Increase
Coffee	4,912,361	5,004,029	91,558	2
Poultry	15,940	101,092	85,152	534
Eggs	59,420	141,635	82,215	138
Milk	41,500	74,925	33,425	81
Beef	802,500	809,925	7,425	1
Pork	3,150	17,000	13,850	440
Platano	51,539	51,539	--	--
Yuca	6,615	6,615	--	--
Cacao	5,130	5,130	--	--
Panela	1,646,025	2,103,150	457,125	28
Corn	2,880	2,880	--	--

Source: Consumer Survey.

Projected Value Added

The projected value added was computed in the
same manner as the base period value added--the projected input was subtracted from the projected output. Projected value added for the sample was Col
$5.5 million as shown in Table 96.

Direct Development Value

Development value refers to the difference between the base and the projected aggregate of gross
farm output for the 50 farms minus the inputs not
derived from the farms. This is essentially the
contribution that rural electrification, through
energy savings and economy of scale, could make to
the gross national product. All input factors except energy were held at a constant ratio to output.
Energy inputs were permitted to fluctuate to reflect the substitution of electric energy for fuels.
Economy of scale resulted from increased farm operations permitted by savings in labor and fuel energy
through farm electrification.

To determine development value, the projected
value added was subtracted from the base value
added. The result showed that rural electrification would make a direct contribution to development. Development value of the 50 farms surveyed
is shown in Table 97.

Rural electrification on all 50 farms in the
sample would have a direct development value of approximately Col $10,217 per farm if all respondents
carried out their intended changes in production
after electricity became available.

Output was at a low level on six of the eight
farms where rural electrification would have a
negative effect on income. Of the two remaining
farms, one had its own hydroelectric plant and base
period operational costs for lighting were computed
at zero. The farm was planning to purchase power

TABLE 96

Projected Value Added for 50 Farms
in Sevilla and Caicedonia
(in pesos)

Farm	Projected Output	Projected Input	Projected Value Added
1	108,867	66,955	41,912
2	314,066	167,072	146,994
3	105,800	90,264	15,536
4	30,985	24,662	6,323
5	63,104	28,309	34,795
6	16,380	14,724	1,656
7	216,000	97,158	118,842
8	14,000	8,082	5,918
9	47,585	21,425	26,160
10	675,000	60,976	614,024
11	65,500	21,705	43,795
12	10,500	6,354	4,146
13	77,000	37,295	39,705
14	79,120	7,928	71,192
15	11,400	2,737	8,663
16	29,705	8,409	21,296
17	38,550	22,303	16,247
18	29,911	25,909	4,002
19	158,900	84,983	73,917
20	31,924	8,453	23,471
21	24,500	21,138	3,362
22	54,840	28,485	26,355
23	14,000	3,925	10,075
24	9,328	3,704	5,624
25	1,545	1,300	245

Farm	Projected Output	Projected Input	Projected Value Added
26	67,320	20,375	46,945
27	1,470,000	461,807	1,008,193
28	590,000	182,509	407,491
29	216,380	98,129	118,251
30	42,860	28,443	14,417
31	39,550	22,524	17,026
32	4,440	3,112	1,328
33	28,240	14,136	14,104
34	385,025	238,775	146,250
35	1,886,250	319,838	1,566,412
36	136,000	75,526	60,474
37	15,300	10,127	5,173
38	91,100	21,825	69,275
39	73,600	26,926	46,674
40	85,100	12,342	72,758
41	53,760	6,210	47,550
42	326,400	124,453	201,947
43	124,990	39,585	85,405
44	32,500	28,700	3,800
45	36,400	29,424	6,976
46	31,305	13,869	17,436
47	142,260	103,139	39,121
48	102,000	15,663	86,337
49	72,880	59,320	13,560
50	35,750	15,253	20,497
Total:	8,317,920	2,836,265	5,481,655

Source: Consumer Survey.

TABLE 97

Direct Development Value of Rural Electrification
on 50 Farms in Sevilla and Caicedonia
(in pesos)

Farm	Base Value Added	Projected Value Added	Development Value
1	26,697	41,912	15,215
2	138,291	146,994	8,703
3	13,507	15,536	2,029
4	5,325	6,323	998
5	21,667	34,795	13,128
6	1,650	1,656	6
7	118,568	118,842	274
8	5,732	5,918	186
9	19,704	26,160	6,456
10	613,907	614,024	117
11	40,535	43,795	3,260
12	3,777	4,146	369
13	26,837	39,705	12,868
14	71,017	71,192	175
15	8,722	8,663	(-59)
16	17,001	21,296	4,295
17	13,076	16,247	3,171
18	3,151	4,002	851
19	67,894	73,917	6,023
20	23,460	23,471	11
21	3,447	3,362	(-85)
22	24,016	26,355	2,339
23	10,079	10,075	(-4)
24	5,302	5,624	322
25	199	245	46

Farm	Base Value Added	Projected Value Added	Development Value
26	44,250	46,945	2,695
27	1,009,920	1,008,193	(-1,727)
28	407,454	407,491	37
29	114,211	118,251	4,040
30	12,877	14,417	1,540
31	15,502	17,026	1,524
32	1,297	1,328	31
33	14,158	14,104	(-54)
34	138,929	146,250	7,321
35	1,170,007	1,566,412	396,405
36	60,142	60,474	332
37	3,744	5,173	1,429
38	69,542	69,275	(-267)
39	46,520	46,674	154
40	72,744	72,758	14
41	47,340	47,550	210
42	200,803	201,947	1,144
43	76,238	85,405	9,167
44	3,946	3,800	(-146)
45	7,326	6,976	(-350)
46	13,809	17,436	3,627
47	36,532	39,121	2,589
48	86,032	86,337	305
49	13,435	13,560	125
50	20,467	20,497	30
Total:	4,970,786	5,481,655	510,869

Source: Consumer Survey.

from the cooperative because the source of energy
would be more reliable and less bother. Thus, the
anticipated use of electricity would be an additional cost. The farm had no plans for increasing production with availability of electricity from the
cooperative.

Candles were the sole source of lights for the
second farm. With the use of 17 light bulbs, 2
radios, 2 irons and 1 refrigerator, the cost of
electric energy obviously would be greater than the
expense of burning candles. Production plans on
the farm were indefinite with the availability of
electricity, therefore, no projection was made for
increased output.

It was apparent from the survey that rural
electrification would have a greater beneficial effect on the more intensively farmed units and on
the large farms that already were consuming substantial amounts of energy. Results did not indicate
that the smaller farms, which were not farmed intensively, would make much contribution to development.
Their costs for electric energy, however, were covered in most cases by increased production or by
savings through the substitution of electricity for
fuels. Therefore, their level of living would be
improved considerably through the use of electric
lights and electrical appliances at little or no
additional cost to the economy.

The direct development value for the sample of
50 farms was Col $510,869. Total investment of for-
eign and local currency in the electric cooperative
was estimated at an equivalent of $1,222,381 with
approximately $681,654 for rural construction.

Rural membership of the cooperative within
three years after energization was estimated at
1,700 of which 680 were commercial farms. Based on
the results of the survey of 50 farms, development
value was projected for the 680 farms. These farms
were considered to be the rural productive members
of the cooperative. Village residential members

and subsistence farms were considered to be the
rural consumptive members.

It was assumed that rural consumptive members
of the cooperative would not increase or decrease
development value of the rural electric cooperative.
Substitution of electric energy for fuels would increase income for some members and decrease it for
others. There was no attempt to determine the development value of rural industrialization as a result of rural electrification. Indications were
that rural industrialization would make a substantial contribution to development after energization
of the cooperative, but it was difficult to estimate the amount of time needed to develop rural industrialization.

Therefore, projecting direct development value
for all commercial farms gave a total value of Col
$6,947,818. Direct development value for the en-
tire rural membership of the cooperative average
Col $4,087 per member. Investment in the rural por-
tion of the electric cooperative was estimated at
Col $9,202,325. This was an average of Col $5,413
per rural connection. The result was that an average investment per connection of Col $5,413 would
produce Col $4,087 annually for development of the
national economy.

Thus, an investment of Col $1.00 in rural elec-
trification was estimated to return Col $.755 to
the Colombian economy within three years after the
availability of electricity and every year thereafter.

For purposes of projecting return from rural
electrification it was assumed that one fourth of
the stated production plans would be carried out
during the first year after electricity became
available. During the second year, it was assumed
the commercial farmers would increase production
half of their stated three-year production goals.
In the third year it was assumed they would produce
three fourths of their goals. During the fourth

year and every year thereafter they would be carrying out their increased production plans completely.

Returns from rural electrification in the
Sevilla-Caicedonia cooperative area can be shown by
determining the present value of future incomes
from carrying out these production plans. In this
analysis the market rate of interest is used as the
discount rate, or the highest rate of return on alternative investments.

Cost of Col $1.00 invested in rural electrifi-
cation represents the value of goods and services
that might be used for alternative purposes. The
economic cost of using goods and services for rural
electrification then becomes the benefits foregone.
That is, the value that would have resulted from
alternative uses.

Under the usual conditions of relatively full
employment there are other uses for the goods and
services used in the rural electrification project.

> In such cases it may reasonably be
> assumed that the goods and services
> used for project purposes are di-
> verted from uses in which their con-
> sumptive or productive value would
> be approximately equal to the prices
> paid for them. Therefore, the mar-
> ket prices of the goods and services
> diverted into project uses may usual-
> ly be regarded as an adequate measure
> of the alternative uses foregone and
> of the economic cost.[14]

Expected returns from alternative investments
are one of the most important factors a developing
country can apply in determining which development
project to select with the capital available.
Countries that lack capital must choose carefully
to obtain maximum earnings on the limited amounts
available. The market rate of interest, therefore,
becomes an important guide in making decisions

concerning capital investments to obtain income in
the future.

The formula for determining the present value,
V, of a sequence of incomes, I, forthcoming to the
economy over 35 years, the length of the investment,
1, with a discount rate, r, can be expressed as
follows: [15]

$$V = \frac{I_1}{(1+r)} + \frac{I_2}{(1+r)^2} + \frac{I_3}{(1+r)^3} + \ldots \ldots \frac{I_{35}}{(1+r)^{35}}$$

Computation of the formula based on Col $1.00
invested in rural electrification in Sevilla-
Caicedonia is shown in Table 98.

> The values attached to benefits and
> costs at their time of accrual, can
> be made comparable only after con-
> version to an equivalent basis for
> time and degree of certainty of oc-
> currence. Interest and discount
> rate allowances provide a means for
> giving monetary expression to differ-
> ences in the time and certainty of
> benefits and costs. Prevailing in-
> terest and discount rates for loans
> and investments usually reflect both
> the "time" and "risk" elements. . . .
> It would be expected . . . that the
> total allowance for risk and interest
> appropriate in the analysis of a Fed-
> eral project would be comparable with
> such allowance for private undertak-
> ings involving similar risk, uncer-
> tainty and longevity.[16]

Using the market rate of interest in Colombia
as the discount rate, the cash flow of returns was
discounted at 14 percent. The interest rate re-
flects scarcity of capital and inflationary movements that have been characteristic of Colombia's
economy, particularly in recent years.

TABLE 98

Present Value of Increases in Gross National Product
over 35 Years Based on Col $1.00 Original
Investment in Rural Electrification

Year	Present Value of Col $1 Discounted at 14%	Stream of Increases in GNP from Rural Electrification	Present Value of Increases in GNP
1966	.8772	.189	.166
1967	.7695	.378	.291
1968	.6750	.566	.383
1969	.5921	.755	.447
1970	.5194	.755	.392
1971	.4556	.755	.344
1972	.3996	.755	.302
1973	.3506	.755	.265
1974	.3075	.755	.232
1975	.2697	.755	.204
1976	.2366	.755	.179
1977	.2076	.755	.157
1978	.1821	.755	.137
1979	.1597	.755	.121
1980	.1401	.755	.106
1981	.1229	.755	.093
1982	.1078	.755	.081
1983	.0946	.755	.071
1984	.0829	.755	.063
1985	.0728	.755	.055
1986	.0638	.755	.048
1987	.0560	.755	.042
1988	.0491	.755	.037
1989	.0431	.755	.033
1990	.0378	.755	.029
1991	.0332	.755	.025
1992	.0291	.755	.022
1993	.0255	.755	.019
1994	.0224	.755	.017
1995	.0196	.755	.015
1996	.0172	.755	.013
1997	.0151	.755	.011
1998	.0132	.755	.010
1999	.0116	.755	.009
2000	.0102	.755	.008
Total:			4.426

Source: Consumer Survey.

If the discounted present value is less than
one, investments purely for economic considerations
should be placed in alternatives more profitable.
If the discounted present value is greater than one,
investments would be more profitable than other investments returning an annuity of 14 percent. Thus,
under competitive conditions for capital, investments would move toward those projects with the
greatest present value of the annual residual income.[17]

If the discounted present value is less than
one, investments in rural electrification will not
increase the gross national product as much as alternative projects would that return 14 percent annually. If the present value of the stream of incomes from rural electrification is greater than
one, alternative investments returning 14 percent
will not be as profitable to growth of the country's
gross national product as would rural electrification. This analysis assumes a constant capital-
output ratio.

Results of the analysis show the present value
of the increases in gross national product over 35
years from an original investment of Col $1.00 in
rural electrification discounted at 14 percent is
Col $4.43. On the basis of this analysis it can be
stated that the return to the Colombian economy
from rural electrification in Sevilla and Caicedonia
will be greater than the investment by a factor of
4.4 to 1.

INITIAL IMPACT

Rural electrification has made it possible for
approximately 500 coffee plantations in the Municipios of Sevilla and Caicedonia to dispulp and
shell coffee beans mechanically. Before electricity, most of these operations were carried out by
hand labor. In addition to mechanization on the
plantations, there have been installed factories
that process soluble coffee. These are the Ginebra,

Vesubio and Principe factories. Also, the Trilla-
dora Aristizabal factory processes coffee for export.

Small food-processing industries in Sevilla
and Caicedonia have traded their wood-heated ovens
for modern electric ovens. Many people in private
homes also have stopped using wood stoves and are
now cooking with electricity. This has helped stop
the indiscriminate felling of trees in the area.
Cutting down trees to obtain wood for fuel was dam-
aging the local forests. The electric cooperative,
in cooperation with CVC, is planning to promote
other programs to protect local resources.

Commercial activity in the towns has increased
substantially as a result of lighting in stores and
on the streets.

Electricity in Sevilla and Caicedonia is being
used in the homes for preparation of food, ironing
of clothes, conservation of perishable foods and
lighting. On farms electricity is being used for
dispulping coffee beans, milking, poultry production and lighting to extend the work day. In town,
electricity is providing power for coffee factories,
shirt factories, pumps and sugar mills. The cooperative has extended lines to three brown-sugar factories with three-phase transformer installations
of 75, 112.5 and 150 KVA. These factories are operating 10 hours a day at least 300 days a year.

Through the use of loan funds the cooperative
imported 10 five-horsepower and 40 three-horsepower
single-phase motors that were not manufactured in
Colombia. The number of motors ordered was based
upon firm commitments from farmers who needed the
motors for dispulping and drying coffee, pumping
water and chopping feed for livestock. It is anticipated that the cooperative also will assist hun-
dreds of other farmers to install smaller one- to
two-horsepower single-phase motors that are manufactured in Colombia.

The manager of the Se-Ca Rural Electric Cooperative, Carlos Arias, reported the impact of the cooperative on social unrest in the area. He wrote,

> Sevilla and Caicedonia in the Department of Valle, Republic of Colombia, are two cities that were greatly affected by the political violence. The social resentment was general, since it was the belief of the people that the government did not want to help them resolve the problems.
>
> At first they [the people of Sevilla and Caicedonia] thought electrification of the poor districts and of the rural areas was just one more promise made by politicians seeking votes. Today, faced with the reality of electrification, they have come to understand that there exists an entity that is interested in their problems. Not only to supply them with electricity, but to intervene for them with government agencies to build schools, construct roads, supply doctors, drugs, credit, etc.
>
> We are doing all these things because we believe that the progress of our people should be harmonious, i.e., in all fields. That is why we are carrying on a vast campaign of cooperative education, in order to develop the spirit of cooperation among the people of the area that comprises the cooperative. In summary, social solidarity has been developed and the resentment of the people that led the two cities to violence has been dispersed.[18]

NOTES

1. Servico Nacional de Aprendizaje, Estudio Socio-Economico de Area del Valle del Cauca (Bogota: SENA, Seccion de Investigaciones, 1962).

2. Asociacion Nacional de Industriales, Cali and the Cauca Valley (Cali: ANDI, 1964), p. 31.

3. Corporacion Autonoma Regional de Cauca, El Sector Agropecuario (Cali: CVC, Division de Planeacion Regional, 1965), p. 15.

4. Ernesto Velez and Ernest Feder, The Lagging Growth of the Cooperative Movement in Colombia (Bogota: Ministerio de Agricultura, August, 1961), p. 16.

5. Servicio Nacional de Aprendizaje, Estudio Socio-Economico de Area del Quindio (Bogota: SENA, Seccion de Investigaciones, 1961).

6. Alonso Moncada, Un Aspecto de la Violencia (Bogota: 1963), p. 8.

7. Libreia Colombiano Camacho Roldan, Colombia en Cifras: Sintesis de la Actividad Economica, Social y Cultural de la Nacion (Bogota; 1963).

8. Jorge Enrique Fajardo Chaves (Comandante del Batallon, Octava Brigada, Ejercito Nacional Republica del Colombia [national army]), letter dated March 12, 1965.

9. Alliance for Progress Commission of Colombia, El Progresso de Colombia Tercer Ano (Bogota: 1964), p. 40.

10. Capitan Cesar Montenegro Cabera (Secretario, Benemeriot Cuerpo de Bomberos Voluntarios [volunteer fire corps], Sevilla), letter report, March, 1965.

11. Corporacion Autonoma Regional del Cauca, Loan Application for the Se-Ca-Rural Electric Cooperative (Cali: CVC, 1963), p. 6.

12.   U.S. Agency for International Development, Contract AID/csd-225 (Washington, AID, 1962), p. 2.

13.   Louis B. Strong, Investigation and Organization of Two Pilot Demonstration Electric Cooperatives (Washington: National Rural Electric Cooperative Association, 1963), p. 14.

14.   Subcommittee on Evaluation Standards, Proposed Practices for Economic Analysis of River Basin Projects (Washington: Report of the Inter-Agency Committee on Water Resources, May, 1958), pp. 8, 9.

15.   Earl O. Heady, Economics of Agricultural Production and Resource Use (Englewood Cliffs, N.J.: Prentice-Hall, 1952).

16.   Subcommittee, op. cit., p. 22.

17.   Earl O. Heady and Luther G. Tweeten, Resource Demand and Structure of the Agricultural Industry (Ames: Iowa State University Press, 1963), p. 407.

18.   Data from a questionnaire completed by Carlos Arias, Manager of the Se-Ca Rural Electric Cooperative, Sevilla, Colombia, and a letter dated April 27, 1970, from Lloyd J. Lake transmitting the questionnaire.

3

COSTA RICA:
ELECTRIFICATION
AND
RURAL
DIVERSIFICATION

The AID loan to Costa Rica for pilot rural electrification projects amounted to nearly $3.5 million. These funds permitted construction of approximately 400 miles of 14.4/24.9 KV primary lines and 400 miles of 120/240 KV secondary and several distribution lines covering approximately 775 square miles. This sum, for the establishment of three rural electric cooperatives in the San Carlos, San Marcos and Guanacaste areas, did not include local contributions nor the cost of power generation facilities provided by the National Institute of Electricity (ICE).

Since the investments in rural electrification competed for the limited resources available in Costa Rica, the U.S. AID Mission in Costa Rica authorized a study to determine the contributions of

───────────

Much of the information appearing in this chapter was taken from a report by Galen C. Moses to the U.S. AID Mission to Costa Rica in 1969. The report was based on Mr. Moses' thesis for the degree of Master of Science in Agriculture, while a

rural electric cooperatives to economic and social
development. This analysis could then help determine the priority such projects should receive in
the future for the allocation of investment funds.
The study was made, through a contract with the
University of Florida, by Galen C. Moses, a graduate student in the Department of Agricultural Economics. His work was supervised by Drs. John
Reynolds, W. W. McPherson and R. W. Bradbury.

The study was concerned with establishing a
methodological framework, as well as providing
bench mark data from which a more detailed study of
the benefits and costs of cooperative rural electrification could be carried out later.

Specific objectives of the study were: (1) to
establish bench marks from which a follow-up study
could measure social and economic change initiated
by the three rural electric cooperatives, (2) to
determine the effect of socioeconomic characteristics on the present and expected uses of electricity in rural electric cooperative areas, (3) to
compare the cost of electricity with alternative
energy sources and (4) to analyze the attitudes of
cooperative members toward the use of electricity
and the cooperative form of organization.

FRAMEWORK FOR ANALYSIS

A review by Mr. Moses of studies concerning
rural electrification in the United States and

---

graduate student in the Department of Agricultural
Economics at the University of Florida. Data and
information are supplemented by a follow-up report
by the manager of the San Marcos Electric Cooperative and the author's personal experience of living
in Costa Rica for two and a half years during the
organization and construction phases of the three
cooperatives.

other countries led to the development of hypotheses concerning the possible effects of rural electrification in an underdeveloped area. These hypotheses were used as the basis for developing a questionnaire to obtain bench mark data from a sample of member households in each of the cooperative areas.

The field survey for this study was conducted from August to November, 1968, in the three rural electric cooperative areas in Costa Rica. At this time, organization of the cooperatives was well established. Membership drives and educational activities had been carried on by cooperative personnel since 1965 and a substantial part of the distribution systems had been constructed.

A questionnaire was developed and pretested in the San Carlos area and the same questionnaire was used in all three cooperative areas. Data were obtained from interviews with a sample of cooperative members in each of the three areas. Mr. Moses personally conducted all interviews in each area. Secondary data were obtained from the agricultural census of 1963 and other published records to provide a summary of the basic climatic and geographic characteristics of each area in relation to their possible effect on the rural electrification projects.

The data obtained from the individual interviews were analyzed to establish bench marks from which socioeconomic change initiated by the rural electric cooperatives could be measured in a follow-up study. Expected household power consumption was estimated for each cooperative member in the sample. The factors affecting expected power consumption were then analyzed by means of regression analysis. Implications as to the benefits to be gained from electricity in the respective cooperative areas were also drawn.

The approach of this study was to identify possible benefits of cooperative rural electrification

in three diverse regions of Costa Rica. Bench mark
data presented in the study may be used as a base
from which to measure change in the respective cooperative areas.

FINDINGS

Regional Benefits

The three areas in which the rural electric
cooperatives were established differed with respect
to their ability to obtain maximum benefits from
the rural electrification projects. Physical, climatic and socioeconomic conditions indicated that
the San Carlos area had greater potential for the
productive application of electricity than the San
Marcos and Guanacaste areas. Agriculturally related industries in San Carlos included coffee
beneficios (places for dispulping and drying coffee
beans), sugar mills, sawmills, a milk receiving
station and a stockyard. Many of these enterprises
were expected to expand their facilities with the
use of electricity from the cooperative. Natural
conditions in the area also indicated a definite
possibility for agricultural diversification and
the introduction of new industries utilizing electric power.

The major constraint to the development of the
San Marcos area, and the productive use of electricity, was the rugged physical features of the
area. The mountainous terrain and poor soils generally limit agricultural production to coffee and
other permanent crops. The lack of diversified
agricultural production reduces the possibilities
for the development of agriculturally related industries utilizing cooperative power. It appeared
that coffee beneficios might derive some benefit
from cooperative electricity as they expanded or
replaced existing hydroelectric or diesel generators. Diversification studies would be necessary
to determine other industrial uses of electricity
in the San Marcos area.

In Guanacaste, the proper management of water resources, facilitated through the use of electric pumps, could greatly increase the agricultural productivity of the area serviced by the rural electric cooperative. Present production of rice, cotton, sugar cane and beef cattle is subject to the hazards of drought or flooding. It was expected that the large-scale farming units would benefit from having electricity for farm machine shops and the equipment to handle agricultural commodities. The use of electricity for the commercial processing of agricultural products was expected following an increase in the capacity of cooperative generation facilities with its tie-in to the national grid.

In all areas, it was anticipated that cooperative power would reduce the large capital outlays made by individuals for the purchase and maintenance of private electric generating facilities. Since, generally, only the more prosperous and progressive farmers and businessmen had private plants, it was expected that savings provided by the purchase of cooperative power would be utilized for the purchase of technological inputs to improve productive capacity.

Domestic Benefits

At the household level, light bulbs and irons were the most common expected purchases of electrical items in all areas. Other popular appliances in the San Carlos and San Marcos areas were stoves, washing machines and refrigerators. A few respondents in Guanacaste expected to purchase television sets.

The estimated average monthly consumption of electricity was similar in all areas at approximately 67 kilowatt-hours per month. The average monthly cost of electric service was estimated to be about ₡ 20 (6.63 colones = $1.00). This estimated average expenditure for cooperative electricity was lower than the cost of present energy from

private generating plants and for those using
kerosene- or gas-operated appliances. However,
electric service from the cooperatives would require higher expenditures for energy by those (primarily peons) using only candles and small quantities of kerosene. It should be emphasized that
these direct cost comparisons do not take into consideration the qualitative factors provided by dependable 24-hour electric service.

Regression analysis revealed that for members
of the Guanacaste Cooperative the most important
factors explaining the expected household consumption of electricity were income, present energy
costs, previous experience with electric service
and education. Only the income variables were
highly significant in the other two areas. In all
areas an increase in income would significantly increase the expected household consumption of electricity. The results of an analysis of the pooled
data indicated that income and education were the
most significant variables explaining expected
household consumption of electricity. This indicates the importance of the income-generating aspect of rural electrification, which permits the
purchase of appliances from which the domestic benefits of electric service may be realized.

The analysis of the expected consumption of
electricity was based on the planned purchases of
household electrical items by members surveyed.
A follow-up study would have the benefit of ob-
serving actual purchases of electrical appliances
as well as obtaining accurate consumption figures
from monthly billings. Actual productive uses
could also be thoroughly investigated.

CONCLUSIONS

Benefits from rural electrification had become
noticeable within a short time after energization.
Despite successful results, however, cooperative
managers must continue to stress the need to use

electricity for productive purposes. Member education activities need to be oriented toward benefits
that can be derived by using electricity to increase production. Members and prospective members
should be thoroughly informed as to the responsi-
bilities and benefits of the cooperative approach
to providing electricity. Secondly, the possibilities for the domestic utilization of electricity
and the feasibility of its application to farm or
business activities need to be stressed.

Education is vital to make the members aware
of the domestic and economically feasible productive uses of electricity. In those areas of Costa
Rica where people had electricity prior to cooperative formation, it was in most cases of very limited application because of the small capacity of
private generating plants. Often it was a question
of using either lights or the electric iron. Thus,
cooperative members must be made aware that cooperative power will be supplied on a dependable 24-
hour basis. This concept will be new to most members.

There is the potential danger that rural electrification may create a rising tide of expecta-
tions within the straits of poverty. Where existing institutions or land tenure practices effec-
tively prevent individuals from making productive
use of electricity, the electric cooperatives must
be leaders in exploring the possibilities for
changing institutional structures. The idea of
productive application of rural electrification
cannot be a reality to the peon without land or
steady employment. The cooperatives must also encourage industrial firms to locate in their areas.
This is true not only to enhance the status of the
cooperative in the eyes of the membership community, but also for its economic survival through load
build-up. Unless the cooperative takes a real role
in improving the economic condition of the poorer
members, the old complaint of development projects
--that they only create a greater economic and social stratification--may arise.

In those areas traditionally characterized by
a patron-peon relationship, the rural electric
cooperatives must take the lead in breaking this
institutional structure. By its very legal nature,
the cooperative ideal upholds the principle that
all members have equal voice and vote. The cooperative should not be allowed to become another
patron in the ages-long succession. This may be
avoided by stressing the self-help nature of cooperative rural electrification. Members may be
made aware that someone does take an interest in
their welfare as well as being led to understand
the extent to which their own purchase of shares
has helped to change previously existing conditions.

Personal contact with the manager is extremely
important in rural electric cooperatives. With
cooperatives the size of those in Costa Rica, it
would seem that the myriad details of construction
supervision and membership education or public relations are too big a job for one man. Consequently (as originally planned through the National Institute of Electricity in Costa Rica), it is sug-
gested for future projects that a technician or
engineer have charge of construction, while the
manager has overall supervision and responsibility,
but with emphasis on his public relations role.

An indication of the influence exerted by the
respective managers and of the direction they may
give to community oriented activities was found in
Guanacaste. The village of Arado, near Santa Cruz,
was typical of other villages in the area, except
that all the houses were neat and brightly painted.
Community members said that this was due to the efforts of the electric cooperative manager in obtaining loans and materials for the painting project stemming from organizational meetings for the
electric cooperative.

One of the objectives of this study was to
analyze the attitudes of rural electric cooperative
members toward the use of electricity and the cooperative form of organization. Only limited

success was obtained in meeting this objective.
Consequently, research is needed to develop measures that would accurately reflect the change in
attitudes of cooperative members before and after
electrification. Factors to be considered might
include attitudes toward the organization of the
cooperative and member confidence in the successful
completion of the project, community cooperation
engendered by the electric cooperatives and the
benefits to be gained from electric service (especially in relation to education).

Positive attitudes toward technological change
and progress are vital prerequisites to economic
development. Consequently, a study revealing the
extent to which a rural electric cooperative can
inspire a positive attitude or desire for change
and community development would further enhance the
priority rural electrification investments should
receive.

In relation to the productive use of electricity, it would be beneficial to determine at what
level of production and in what types of enterprises electricity makes the greatest contribution
in developing countries. This would require an
in-depth analysis of specific enterprises in a
given area, with a careful consideration of the
availability and cost of labor. Such a study would
not only indicate those regions most able to benefit from electricity, but would also indicate to
producers in an area the economic returns to be
expected from electric service.

From results of this study it is evident that
rural electrification can be important to Costa
Rica, largely because of the extent to which the
economy of the country is agriculturally oriented.
Increased productivity, greater processing of agriculture products for export, and the development of
new industries with electric power, as well as improved living conditions that might encourage
people to move from the crowded Meseta Central,
indicate benefits to the nation that may occur.

CHAPTER

4

ECUADOR:
ELECTRIFICATION
AND
RURAL
INDUSTRIALIZATION

STRUCTURE OF THE RURAL ECONOMY

Ecuador's economy is based on agriculture.
Farm production accounts for over 90 percent of its
foreign exchange earnings and about 33 percent of
the national product. General development of the
country is greatly dependent upon the state of production and trade in a few agricultural commodities.

General Characteristics

Ecuador is located on the west coast of South
America on the equator. It is bounded by Colombia
on the north, Peru on the east and south and the
Pacific Ocean on the west. Ecuador's land area is
estimated at 105,000 square miles, approximately
the size of Colorado. It is second smallest of the
South American republics. Only Uruguay has less
land area.

In spite of its equatorial location, Ecuador's
climate is greatly modified by the Pacific Ocean
and the higher altitudes. The climate varies, becoming progressively drier toward the south. Desert
conditions prevail in the coastal area adjoining

Peru. In general, there are two seasons--a rainy
season from December through April, followed by a
moderate, dry period.

Some 60 percent of Ecuador's population,
placed at 5.7 million in 1968, are classified as
rural. Of the total population some 40 percent are
American Indian, another 40 percent mestizo, 10
percent white and 5 percent Negro.

Ecuador is preponderantly Roman Catholic, but
church and state are legally separated. The present government is a military junta that assumed
power on July 11, 1963. The four-man junta de-
clared martial law, suspended constitutional guar-
antees and outlawed the Communist Party. Later
sweeping social, economic and administrative reforms were announced and the constitution was re-
instated.

The basic monetary unit is the sucre (S/.),
divided into 100 centavos. The official exchange
rate is 17.82 sucres per U.S. dollar, buying rate,
and 18.18 sucres per U.S. dollar, selling rate.

Ecuador is among the less developed countries
of Latin America. For many of its people the level
of living is low.

Agriculture's Role

Agriculture is the largest single sector of
Ecuador's economy. It employs over half of the
active labor force and provides one third of the
gross national product.

Bananas, cacao and coffee provide about 85
percent of total export earnings. In recent years
Ecuador has been the world's largest supplier of
bananas. Rice and sugar have also been important
export items. The country grows a sufficient vari-
ety of fruits and vegetables for its own domestic
use. Potatoes are the most important vegetable

crop. Oranges and pineapples are exported. Except
for wheat and oats, Ecuador raises a sufficient
amount of food grains for domestic consumption.

Most of Ecuador's area is covered with forests.
But logging and mill operations are on a compara-
tively small scale. Balsa wood and tagua nuts, the
source of vegetable ivory, are Ecuador's principal
exports of forest products. Mangrove lumber, kapok,
cinchona bark and other tropical woods and forest
products are gathered for export.

Some of the richest fishing grounds in the
world are off the coast of Ecuador. The bulk of
production of fish and shellfish is frozen and exported. Ecuador is the only Andean republic in
whose economy mineral production does not play an
important role. The only mining operations of any
significance are those of gold. Petroleum production is of significance to the economy and the government is seeking means of stimulating domestic
production so that foreign exchange expenditures
for petroleum imports may be reduced.

Agricultural Development

The future of Ecuador's economy lies in the
ability of the government, and its people, to develop the resources of agriculture by increasing
productivity, diversifying its production base, employing modern technology now available, training
its manpower and developing domestic as well as
foreign markets.

Agriculture has a three-fold role in Ecuador's
overall development. First, agriculture can contribute to a better livelihood for the large percentage of the population who derive their income
directly from agriculture. Second, agriculture can
contribute to a better nutrition for the people of
Ecuador. Third, agriculture can contribute more
foreign exchange earnings for the overall development of Ecuador.

If one objective of economic development is to improve the level of living, this can be done most directly by helping those engaged in agriculture to gain a better return for their efforts. In many developing countries, the rural population has lagged behind in the improved standard of living achieved as the nations have advanced. Helping agriculture to produce more, and market more efficiently, can directly help the nation achieve the dietary standard needed for a more healthful and productive life.

Agriculture accounts for about 90 percent of the country's foreign exchange earnings. Ecuador's National Planning Board has called this foreign exchange the dynamic factor in the nation's development, making possible importation of needed goods and equipment for industry and building the nation's infrastructure. Efforts to increase agricultural exports will have a direct impact on the country's overall development process.

SOCIOECONOMIC CONDITIONS IN THE PROJECT AREA

Until 1938, Santo Domingo, Ecuador, was an isolated area populated only by uneducated Indians. After construction of a road between Santo Domingo and Quito, the capital of Ecuador, settlement by other Ecuadorians began. Later road connections to Esmeraldas and Guayaquil initiated a banana boom that has been the mainstay of the Santo Domingo economy.

Geography and Climate

Santo Domingo is located 78 miles west of Quito in Ecuador's coastal region. The village of Santo Domingo is in the Province (equivalent to a state) of Pichincha, in the Canton (county) of Quito, and in the Parroquia (township) of Santo Domingo.

Land in the Santo Domingo area is relatively
level, although there are steep hills in some
places. The area is located at the foot of a mountain chain and next to the country's coast on the
Pacific Ocean.

Elevation is 1,600 feet. Months of the rainy
season include January, February, March, April and
May. Months of the dry season include November
and December. Average annual rainfall is about
200 inches. Annual maximum temperature is around
67°F., while the yearly minimum temperature is
about 61°F.

Population and Education

Population of the Santo Domingo area, some
20,000 at the time of the yield study, is growing
rapidly. In the village of Santo Domingo there are
more than 10,000 residents, while in the rural
areas within 25 miles there are an additional
10,000. These rural residents live primarily on
four main roads leading from Santo Domingo.

Literacy in the Santo Domingo area is estimated at better than 50 percent. In the village of
Santo Domingo there are two Catholic schools, two
government schools and one technical high school.
A reading and writing adult education program was
started in the village about two years ago.

Community Welfare and Leadership

Although water in Santo Domingo is considered
potable, most people boil their drinking water.
There are some sewage facilities.

In Santo Domingo there were ten doctors and
ten dentists--a relatively high ratio of physicians
per population. There also were several nurses and
midwives and three pharmacists. There was one general hospital, one social welfare hospital and
three independent clinics.

There was no community center but there were
several civic associations. Cooperatives in the
township of Santo Domingo area had a membership of
approximately 60,000. This included both farm and
town cooperatives.

There were roughly 2,000 homes in Santo Domingo. Approximately 85 percent of the houses had
tile roofs; 10 percent had zinc and 5 percent were
thatched. Roughly 80 percent of the homes had wood
floors and 20 percent were made of concrete. Ninety percent of the houses had wood siding, while the
remaining 10 percent were of masonry. Most of the
houses had two floors and the average house had
four or five rooms.

Leadership in the community was vested with
the Junta Mejoras (the community development group),
the board of directors of the rural electric cooperative and the Catholic Church.

Transportation and Communication

In 1963 a modern two-lane road through the
mountains from Quito to Santo Domingo was completed.
Another highway south from Santo Domingo to Quevedo
was opened soon afterward connecting the Santo Domingo area with the ports of Guayaquil and Manta.
Both of these highways were financed by AID. The
roads to Guayaquil, northwest to Esmeraldas, and
west to Chone and Bahia were being improved through
local financing. Streets in Santo Domingo, except
the highways passing through the village, were un-
paved.

There was a mail system in Santo Domingo, but
no delivery to the homes. There was a telephone
system, a telegraph system and the village had
three radio stations. The mountains between Quito
and Santo Domingo were too high for reception from
Quito's television station.

Employment and Wages

Principal areas of employment in Santo Domingo were in the Colonization Program, commercial activities and small industries. Industry in the area included rice mills, sawmills, two soft drink plants, one coffee mill, one spaghetti plant, an ice plant and an ice cream plant.

Generally there was no season of unemployment. Because of the climate and the nature of economic activities there was work to be found during most of the year. It was estimated that there were about three male workers and one female worker in an average family.

Migratory workers earned between S/.18 and S/.22 per day without meals. With three meals per day they earn about S/.15. They were paid on the basis of a six-and-a-half-day week. A farm foreman earned between S/.700 and S/.900 per month.

Production and Marketing

Agriculture supported the Santo Domingo area. Within a 25-mile radius of the village of Santo Domingo there were 374,000 acres of rich agricultural land--most of which had not been cleared for farming.

Principal cash crops grown in the area included bananas, beef cattle, coffee, cocoa, African palm, lumber, pineapples, vegetables and citrus fruits. Food crops included primarily platano, bananas, yuca, rice and meat consisting mainly of beef and wild animals. It was estimated that rice consumption was about 1.5 pounds per person per week.

Guayaquil was the principal market for most commercial crops; however, Quito was the main

market for alcohol made from sugar cane, lumber and
fruits such as pineapples. Guayaquil is 75 miles
from Santo Domingo, Quito is 78 miles. Transportation to the markets was by truck.

Bananas sold for S/.4.50 for a 42-pound box at
the farm. Transporting the bananas to Guayaquil
cost S/.3.70 per box. Beef sold for S/.1.90 per
pound live weight at the farm. Transportation cost
S/.150 per head. Coffee sold for S/.1 per pound
cherry. Cocoa sold for S/.250 per 100 pounds.
Transportation costs for both coffee and cocoa to
Guayaquil was S/.5 per 100-pound sack.

Income, Savings and Investment

Typical annual income for a migratory family
or small farmer in the Santo Domingo area was
S/.5,000. The typical debt for a village family
was the equivalent of one month's salary or approximately S/.400. Most of the families saved a little but spent their savings on parties. There was
very little savings for investment purposes, and
that was used to purchase land.

Santo Domingo had two banks. It was estimated
that approximately 50 percent of the families had
bank accounts. The largest bank had a savings balance of S/.1 million and deposits amounting to
S/.4 million.

Electric Energy

From 1960 to 1964 the Municipality of Quito
supplied electric energy to the village of Santo
Domingo. The system was operated by Empresa Electrica Quito. Two 150 KW diesel generators were the
source of power. Electricity was available only
to one fourth of the homes from 6 p.m. until 2 a.m.
Lighting and a few small appliances were the only
uses of the electric power.

On March 20, 1964, the municipal system was
turned over to the rural electric cooperative. The
cooperative began operating the diesel engines 24

hours a day and expanded operations with materials
donated by rural electric cooperatives in the
United States. This created a need for more electric power. To solve the power shortage the cooperative leased a 200-kilowatt generator.

DEVELOPMENT OF THE COOPERATIVE

The Santo Domingo Rural Electric Cooperative
was developed to help achieve an increase in agricultural and industrial production and to help expand the economic and social infrastructure in the
Santo Domingo area. Loan funds to develop the
project were approved by the Agency for International Development in order to make possible a significant improvement in the potential of Santo Domingo as a trading center. It also was thought the
rural electric cooperative would assist development
of the cooperative movement in Ecuador.

Initial Investigation

In January, 1963, Charles Stewart, manager of
the Warren Rural Electric Cooperative Corporation
(RECC), of Bowling Green, Kentucky, began a one-
month assignment in Ecuador to determine the possibility for establishing one or more pilot rural
electric cooperatives. His assignment was financed
by the AID Mission to Ecuador and Stewart was representing the National Rural Electric Cooperative
Association (NRECA).

In his final report, Stewart observed that
there was a severe shortage of electric power
throughout Ecuador and that most of the power was
generated at very high cost. Stewart found that
the people lacked confidence in the national government and, to a lesser extent, in the local government but that they were receptive to the idea of
cooperatives. He recommended development of cooperative rural electrification in Ecuador.

In August, 1963, John Taylor, former manager
of Walton Electric Membership Corporation (EMC), of

Monroe, Georgia, began an assignment in Ecuador under the AID/NRECA program to plan and begin organization of a pilot rural electric cooperative. He
was joined a month later by Ervin Blish, engineer
for the Central Kansas Electric Cooperative, of
Great Bend, Kansas. Blish was to conduct an engineering and feasibility study for the cooperative.

     Taylor and Blish, along with AID and Ecuador-
ian Government personnel, surveyed several areas in
Ecuador. They decided to begin the country's rural
electrification program with a pilot rural electric
cooperative in Santo Domingo. Taylor stated in his
final report that rural electric cooperatives in
Ecuador should include generation and distribution
facilities.

     On October 13, 1963, the Santo Domingo area
was officially selected as the pilot project area.

Engineering Aspects

     The initial project consisted of construction
of an electric generating plant and installation of
related equipment to expand capacity to 1,650 KW.
It also provided for a substation to transform the
voltage to 7.2/12.5 KV, 115 miles of three-phase
distribution lines, 27.5 miles of single-phase line
and the associated transformers and electric service drops to serve the town of Santo Domingo and
surrounding areas.

     On March 20, 1964, the cooperative obtained
ownership of the existing facilities in Santo Domingo, consisting of a diesel electric generating
plant of 300 KW capacity, a set-up substation of
374 KVA capacity, and the electric distribution
system in Santo Domingo. The two generators were
retained until larger generators could be installed. The balance of the property was of no
value and was to be replaced eventually by more
modern equipment.

A technical description of the engineering aspect is as follows:

Power Source—Cooperative 1,650 KW generating plant consisting of three 450 KW diesel, two 150 KW diesel.

Estimated Cost of Power—0.38 sucres or 2.1 cents.

Substation—1,500 KVA 480/7,200 Volts.

System Primary Voltage—7.2/12.5 KV 60 cycle.

Type of System—Radial.

Size of System—
   3 miles 7.2/12.5 KV three-phase line in Santo Domingo
   112 miles 7.2/12.5 KV three-phase rural line
   27.5 miles 7.2/KV single-phase rural line
   1,400 service drops and associated 12/240 secondary

Installed Transformer Capacity—920 KVA in Santo Domingo and 870 KVA in the rural area.

Construction Standards—Similar to REA standards modified to meet local conditions.

Code Requirements—No code requirements in Ecuador but lines to be designed to U.S. NESC requirements.

Loading—NESC light loading.

System Demand—
   1964 - 244 KW
   1967 - 953 KW
   1973 - 1653 KW

Average Kilowatt-Hours per Consumer—
   1964 - 50 KWH
   1967 - 80 KWH
   1973 - 125 KWH

Consumers--
	Residential	Commercial
1964	- 560	240
1967	- 1,990	510
1973	- 2,659	600

System Capacity--The lines were to have capacity to serve 3,259 consumers at average of 125 KWH/month with not more than 7.4 percent regulation, adequate for at least 10 years.

Sectionalizing--Oil circuit reclosers.

Engineering services were to be performed by INECEL (Instituto Ecuatoriano de Electrificacion). INECEL was established in 1961 and is an autonomous government agency working with the Ecuadorian Ministerio de Fomento and is devoted to the planning, financing, construction and operation of electric enterprises in the country. To carry out its operations, INECEL obtained funds through surcharges on electric utility revenues of operating utilities in Ecuador. It was authorized to invest its own resources, and to own and operate electric enterprises for the economic development of the country.

Financial Aspects

The estimated total cost of the project was $1,269,000. To cover a portion of the local contribution, cooperative members assessed themselves, by means of membership fees, a total of $90,000. The financial plan was as shown in Table 99.

The cooperative was to provide up to 50,000 KWH annually of free municipal street lighting for a period of five years; this was the equivalent of an additional local contribution of $125,000 and was considered a fair price and valuation of the franchise, equipment and distribution network received by the Santo Domingo Rural Electric Cooperative. The AID loan amounted to $650,000, of which $349,000 was foreign exchange. In addition to these funds, there was to be assistance to the

TABLE 99

Financial Plan for the Santo Domingo Rural
Electric Cooperative, 1964
(in dollars)

Source of Financing	Local Costs	Foreign Costs	Total Costs
Borrower (existing equipment)	$125,000		
Borrower (new financing)	90,000		$215,000
AID Loan	301,000	$349,000	650,000
AID Grant		128,000	128,000
Donated equipment and material		276,000	276,000
Total:	$516,000	$753,000	$1,269,000

Source: Loan Application.

cooperative in the form of $53,000 of AID-grant
funds to provide management consulting services.
Included in the cost of the project was a contribution in the form of materials made by the Kentucky
Rural Electric Association valued at $91,000.
Three 450 KW generating sets were obtained from
U.S. Government excess surplus property in San
Diego, California, without cost except for transportation from the Ecuadorian port to the site of
installation; their acquisition valuation was
$369,000, which was reduced by 50 percent for book-
keeping valuation purposes.

On August 30, 1964, AID authorized loan funds
amounting to $650,000 to INECEL to construct the
Santo Domingo Rural Electric Cooperative.

Terms of the $650,000 loan to INECEL were: 40
years including a 10-year grace period with interest at .75 percent for 6 years and 2 percent thereafter. INECEL in turn was to lend the funds to the
Santo Domingo Rural Electric Cooperative at the
following terms: 30 years, including a 6-year
grace period, with interest at 1.50 percent during
the grace period and 2.75 percent thereafter.

Repayment of the loan was to be in dollars and
the loan was guaranteed by the Government of Ecuador. It was decided that the cooperative should
assume maintenance of value risk rather than the
government. It was traditional for Ecuadorian municipalities and private electric companies to assume this risk through normal supplier credit or
other external loans.

Organization

The former power supplier in Santo Domingo,
Empresa Electrica Quito, did not have funds to repair one of the diesel generators (estimated cost
of repair was $1,000). Nor did the Empresa have
funds to improve the distribution system or to connect homes located near the existing lines.

Community leaders in Santo Domingo wanted to
improve their electric system, but they did not
know how. After discussing the situation with U.S.
rural electrification specialists Taylor and Blish,
Gustavo Riofrio of the AID Mission and David Leon
of INECEL, a plan was developed for the community
to purchase the entire electric system on a long-
term payment plan. The system would be operated by
the community rather than the municipality.

Leaders in Santo Domingo proposed to raise
locally S/.310,000 (approximately $17,222). Funds
were to be used to repair the generator, extend
primary lines 1.6 miles, connect 400 services along
existing lines, provide 24-hour electric service,
operating funds and to purchase transformers,
breakers and station equipment.

In order to carry out this plan it was necessary to legally organize a rural electric cooperative. This required signing of members and the
payment of membership fees, holding a member meeting to organize the cooperative, adoption of bylaws
by the members, legally recording the bylaws and
election of a board of directors and vigilance committee.

On January 10, 1964, the Santo Domingo Rural
Electric Cooperative was legally recognized by the
Government of Ecuador. Work then began to complete
the member sign-up campaign in the town of Santo
Domingo. Town and rural areas were then combined
into one large project and a loan application was
prepared for financing the project. The loan application was submitted to the AID Mission in May,
1964.

Planned Construction

Construction of the project was to be by contract. The cooperative would furnish all materials
and the contractor would furnish labor and equipment. Ecuador had several contractors who were
qualified and experienced in this type of construction.

No unusual construction problems were expected.
Roads in the area were considered adequate for
transportation of materials and equipment. Climatic and geological conditions were not expected
to adversely affect construction of the project.

Materials, with the exception of poles, were
to be obtained in the United States. Since there
were no wood treatment plants in Ecuador capable of
treating pole-length timber, concrete poles were
used for line construction. However, their cost
was relatively high.

Single-phase 1.5 and 3 KVA transformers and
2-wire meters were to be obtained for the cost of
rehabilitation and transportation from the Kentucky

Rural Electric Cooperative Corporation in the United States. These transformers and meters were the small sizes no longer used on rural systems in the United States, but adequate for a system where the demand for power would be small during the first years of operation.

Transportation and rehabilitation of the equipment was to be borne by the Santo Domingo Rural Electric Cooperative through their own resources and before the loan agreement. After loan funds became available, it was anticipated that loan funding would be used where dollar costs were incurred. These transformers and meters were to be given to the cooperative as part of a program instituted by the U.S. rural electric cooperatives to help rural electrification in less developed countries.

Three 450 KW diesel-electric generators were to be obtained from U.S. government surplus. The generators were located in San Diego, California.

Construction of the project was to cover an estimated period of 14 months. It was to include rural member sign-up, staking of the lines, ordering and receiving materials, construction and energization of the lines. It was planned to energize sections of the lines as they were completed so that electric service could be received by new members as quickly as possible.

Assuming that the loan agreement was signed in June, 1964, and conditions precedent including the arrival of a U.S. consulting engineer had been met by the end of September, 1964, the 14-month construction schedule listed in the feasibility study would have been as follows:

Rural member sign-up--Sept. through Nov., 1964.
Manufacture poles--Nov., 1964 through Jan., 1965.
Stake line and prepare contract--Sept., 1964-March, 1965.

Order material--January, 1965.
Receive material--Feb.-June, 1965.
Publish bid requirements--March, 1965.
Review and approve bids--March-May, 1965.
Construction--May-Nov., 1965.
Energize consumers--June-Nov., 1965.

Actual construction, however, was approximately two
years behind the anticipated schedule.

Technical Assistance

A. U.S. rural electrification specialist began
providing technical assistance to the rural electric
cooperative immediately following the feasibility
study. This assistance was provided by a grant
from the AID Mission. These services were to include: (1) training and supervision of management
personnel; (2) assisting the cooperative in sign-up
of rural members; (3) coordinating cooperative activities with the engineering and construction
phase of the project; and (4) after construction of
the project, assisting the cooperative in its operation through continued training of operation and
management personnel.

In addition to the management consultant, a
U.S. engineering consultant was to be obtained by
INECEL for a period of 18 months. The cost of the
consultant was to be to the account of INECEL, but
the cooperative could be charged for its proportionate share. Funds for the engineering consultant
were included in the loan. Duties of the engineering consultant were to include: (1) training and
supervision of engineering personnel; (2) training
and organization of construction crews; (3) technical supervision of construction, operation and
maintenance; (4) reviewing and approving all plans,
specifications and contracts in connection with
construction of the project, together with an INECEL
engineer; (5) approving selection and purchase of
proper and approved materials to construct the
project; (6) preparation of monthly and quarterly
reports on progress of construction; and (7)

certification of completion of work in accordance
with plans and specifications and correctness of
pay quantities.

INITIAL OPERATION

While the Santo Domingo Rural Electric Cooperative was energized on March 20, 1964, there still
was no farm electrification in October, 1965. Use
of equipment and materials donated by the U.S. rural electric cooperatives permitted the cooperative
to extend the distribution system only in the village of Santo Domingo and to begin 24-hour electric
service. At the time of the field study the system
had been operating under the cooperative arrangement for 18 months.

Donation of Materials

The loan agreement for $650,000 was signed on
August 30, 1964, rather than in June as had been
assumed might be possible. Other delays in meeting
conditions precedent to the release of funds prevented the construction schedule from being carried
out as planned.

Construction of a temporary system in the village of Santo Domingo, however, was accomplished
with the use of local poles and equipment donated
by the Kentucky rural electric cooperatives. Local
wood poles would need to be replaced within a few
years, but the outgrown equipment donated by the
Kentucky cooperatives should remain serviceable for
several years.

As a result of the cooperation of the Kentucky
rural electric cooperatives, the state of Kentucky
and the country of Ecuador were paired as Partners
of the Alliance. The story is a true example of
cooperation.

Soon after Charles Stewart returned to Kentucky after completing the original study of rural
electrification in Ecuador, he was host to a group

of Latin American officials who had come to the
United States to attend a course on "Organization
and Operation of Rural Electric Cooperatives." The
course is given annually by AID, NRECA and its member rural electric cooperatives, the Rural Electrification Administration in the U.S. Department of
Agriculture and the International Training Center
at the University of Wisconsin.

Included in the group were Gustavo Riofrio of
the AID Mission to Ecuador and Jaime Castro of
INECEL. While visiting the rural electric coopera-
tives in Kentucky, they urged the Kentucky Rural
Electric Cooperative Corporation (KRECC) to adopt
Ecuador and to help make it a focal point for em-
phasis in developing rural electrification in Latin
America.

The KRECC reacted quickly. A survey was taken
of all the rural electric systems in the state to
determine what surplus electric line equipment could
be donated to Ecuador. Prior investigation had revealed that the Santo Domingo Cooperative could use
any kind of surplus or outgrown material and equipment available. Surplus materials, materials that
Kentucky's rural electric cooperatives had outgrown
and that were of no particular value except for
junk, were collected in a central point at the
KRECC warehouse in Louisville. These materials
were checked, repaired, inventoried and made ready
for shipment to Ecuador.

Early in 1964, a shipment of some 42,000
pounds of transformers, meters, meter sockets, con-
ductor and hardware items valued at only a few
thousand dollars as unusable equipment was loaded
on KRECC trucks for the trip to Gulfport, Missis-
sippi, where it was transferred to a ship bound for
Ecuador. About $8,000 in equipment not available
as surplus was bought by the cooperative and included in the shipment. This was purchased and
shipped at cost by KRECC.

The Effo Banana Sales Corporation of Gulfport
agreed to carry the equipment to Ecuador free of

charge aboard its ship Bodetal. The Effo ships
bring bananas to this country and usually return
empty. Instead of water for ballast, the Bodetal
carried materials and equipment for the Santo Domingo Cooperative.

Landing at Esmeraldas on June 9, 1964, the material was unloaded by native labor and was trucked
inland 100 miles to Santo Domingo. The use of
trucks to haul the equipment was donated as were
the services of the truck drivers. Through the use
of this equipment, the Santo Domingo Cooperative
was able to build 59 spans of three-phase primary
line to improve voltage.

Membership and Costs

At the time of energization there were 400 cooperative members. Six months later membership had
grown to 736 and at the end of one year there were
815 members. In October, 1965, at the time of the
field trip and 18 months after beginning operations,
the cooperative had 963 members. About 200 members
lived in the rural areas while the remainder lived
in Santo Domingo. At that time there were 631 members receiving electricity and 332 not receiving
electric service.

Also at that time, 18 months after energization, there were 646 meters connected or consumers
in the Santo Domingo Cooperative. With 631 members
receiving electricity, this meant that 15 consumers
had not become members of the cooperative. Nonmembers of the cooperative must pay an additional
charge equal to 20 percent of their monthly bill.
Approximately half of the nonmembers were classified
as commercial and half were residential.

When the cooperative began operations on
March 20, 1964, there were 374 consumers. Six
months later there were 560 and within one year
there were 614 meters connected. Table 100 shows
the classification of consumers in October, 1965.

TABLE 100

Classification of Consumers and Minimum Monthly
Consumption in the Santo Domingo Rural
Electric Cooperative, October, 1965

Classification	Minimum KWH Per Month	No. of Consumers
Residential-1	6	78
Residential-2	20	192
Residential-3	70	--
Commercial-1	10	46
Commercial-2	20	296
Commercial-3	75	28
Industrial	--	2
Official	120	4
Total:		646

Source: Cooperative records.

Initial cost to receive electricity was relatively high. Average minimum cost per consumer was
approximately S/.630 (about $35) excluding cost of
wiring the house. These were the costs that had to
be paid by the consumer before the cooperative
would provide electric service. A breakdown of
membership and connection fees is shown in Table
101.

Shares in the cooperative, as well as the de-
posit for the meter, were to be refundable to the
consumer upon termination of electric service. In
order for the cooperative to meet the requirement
of 20 percent local capital imposed by the loan
agreement it was necessary to sell shares in the
cooperative. Number of shares to be purchased per
consumer depended upon the kilowatt-hour usage.
While the minimum number of shares per residential
consumer was three, the maximum was ten. If a

TABLE 101

Membership and Electric Service Connection
Fees per Consumer in Santo Domingo, 1965

Item	Value in Sucres	Value in Dollars
Membership fee	50	2.77
Shares ea. S/.100 (minimum of 3)	300	16.67
Deposit for meter	130	7.22
Meter installation fee	75	4.17
Wire from pole to house, switch, fuse holder and insulator	75*	4.17
Total payment to cooperative:	630	35.00
Approximate cost of wiring house	200	11.11
Total service cost:	830	46.11

*Estimated on the basis of S/.1.00 per foot of
wire, S/.30.00 for one switch, S/.9.00 for one fuse
holder and S/.10.00 to S/.15.00 for three or four
insulators.

Source: Cooperative records.

consumer were required to purchase the maximum number of shares, his total payment to the cooperative
in advance of electric service would be approximately S/.1,330 or roughly $73.89.

Electric energy lost on the temporary distribution lines was approximately 20 percent.

The cost of generating electric energy, not
including depreciation, was estimated at S/.0.39
per KWH. Including depreciation, the cost would
have been roughly S/.0.50. At the same time the
cooperative was paying S/.0.50 to generate electricity it was selling power to two industrial consumers for less than the generation cost. During
September, 1965, the smallest industrial consumer
paid an average of S/.0.48 per KWH while the largest

industrial consumer paid an average of S/.0.45 per
KWH.

Industrial rates depended upon KW demand. For
example the ice cream plant had the following bill
during September, 1965:

10 KW, each S/.17.00	S/.170.00
500 KWH, each 0.41	205.00
2,490 KWH, each 0.38	986.00
INECEL tax, .02 per KWH	58.80
	$1,420.80

Rates for other types of consumers depended
upon the classification of the consumer and the
amount of electricity used. Consumers were classified as residential, commercial and official as
shown in Table 102.

Payment of monthly electric bills was handled
in the following manner. A consumer was asked to
go to the electric cooperative office and pay his
bill by the 18th of each month. If he had not done
this the cooperative delivered a reminder of the
bill to his home. The consumer then had to pay the
bill by the 21st. If he had not paid by the 21st,
the cooperative would disconnect the meter on the
22nd.

About 25 percent of the consumers paid their
bills by the 18th of the month at the cooperative
office. Most of the consumers paid their bills by
the 21st day or before being disconnected. On October 22, 1965, for example, 577 consumers had paid
and 69 consumers had not paid their monthly bill.
At 8:30 a.m. on October 22, however, when the cooperative opened its office, 19 of the 69 consumers
were waiting to pay their bills. Their meters were
not disconnected. Four other consumers complained
about operations of their meters and the cooperative
determined that the meters were faulty. These consumers were not disconnected. Forty meters were
disconnected, but 28 were reconnected within a few
days. The reconnection fee for each meter was S/.20.

TABLE 102

Residential, Commercial and Official Government Rates
for Electric Service in Santo Domingo, 1965
(value in sucres)

Class	Monthly Minimum		Next		Next		Next	
	KWH	Value	KWH	Value	KWH	Value	KWH	Value
R-1	6	5.00	--	--	--	--	6	0.70*
R-2	20	13.60	10	0.68*	30	0.64*	60	0.59*
R-3	70	50.00	--	--	--	--	70	0.46*
C-1	10	8.00	--	--	--	--	10	1.20*
C-2	20	18.00	10	1.15*	30	1.05*	60	0.90*
C-3	75	80.00	--	--	--	--	75	0.87*
O-1	120	101.00	180	0.80*	200	0.70*	500	0.60*

*Cost per KWH.

Source: Cooperative records.

Six other consumers were delinquent in payment
of their monthly bills, but they were not disconnected. The local hotel was applying for an industrial rate and waiting for the outcome of its application before making payment. Other delinquent
consumers included the hospital, the police station,
the Government Telegraph Office, the Government
Public Works Office and the Municipal Technical
School. Some of these consumers were several
months in arrears, but the cooperative felt it in
the public interest not to disconnect the meters.

Energy Consumption

In March, 1964, there were 374 consumers but
only 350 meters. This meant that 24 consumers were
receiving electricity without being metered. The
cooperative required that every consumer have a meter to determine the amount of electricity used.
Consequently, meters were installed so that the
number of meters was equal to the number of consumers.

Consumption of energy during the first month
the cooperative assumed operations of the distribution system was 53 KWH per consumer. During April,
1964, electric service was available 24 hours a day.
Consumption of electricity jumped to over 100 KWH
per consumer. Since then consumption has fluctuated
but generally remained around 100 KWH per consumer
per month. Table 103 shows energy consumption and
sales from March, 1964, through September, 1965.

Management

In October, 1965, the cooperative was staffed
with 15 employees. The staff worked 44 hours during a five-and-a-half day work week. Members of
the staff included one manager, five office employees, four plant employees, three linemen, one su-
perintendent and one driver. In addition, two
Peace Corps Volunteers were helping the cooperative.
One Peace Corps Volunteer was a mechanical engineer,
the other was an electrician.

TABLE 103

Electric Energy Consumption and Sales in
Santo Domingo from March, 1964,
through September, 1965

Year & Mo.	No. of Con- sumers	KWH Sold	Consumption per Consumer	Energy Sales (S/.)
1964:				
March	374	20,000	53	18,500
April	374	43,308	116	35,750
May	*	45,819	*	37,476
June	*	42,065	*	34,043
July	*	45,890	*	38,416
August	*	55,253	*	44,534
Sept.	529	63,248	119	50,095
Oct.	554	70,534	127	54,466
Nov.	571	57,083	100	45,927
Dec.	575	59,370	103	47,565
1965:				
Jan.	601	71,444	119	56,977
Feb.	604	69,104	114	52,858
March	614	59,681	97	50,834
April	624	79,469	127	63,533
May	637	76,897	121	61,049
June	642	78,133	122	62,156
July	646	74,980	116	61,175
August	644	75,152	117	62,899
Sept.	646	62,863	97	55,784

*Data not available.

Source: Cooperative records.

The manager of the cooperative had been a dentist by profession before assuming administrative responsibility of the cooperative, and it was reported that he was continuing operation of the dental office while serving as manager of the cooperative. Salaries of various job classifications in the cooperative were as shown in Table 104.

The President of the Board of Directors was a young farmer, age 33, living about five miles from the village of Santo Domingo. He spoke English fluently and had graduated from a university in Toronto, Canada, with a degree in agronomy.

TABLE 104

Salaries for Various Job Classifications
in the Santo Domingo Rural Electric
Cooperative, October, 1965

Job Classification	Salary per Mo. in Sucres	Salary per Mo. in Dollars
Manager	4,000	222
Plant Superintendent	2,500	139
Accountant	2,500	139
Secretary	1,200	67
Head Lineman	1,430	79
Assistant Lineman	700	39
Plant Operator	990	55
Janitor	800	44
Driver	1,500	83

Source: Cooperative records.

The vice president of the board was owner and operator of an ice plant and gasoline station and the largest industrial consumer in the cooperative. The treasurer of the board operated a gasoline station and auto shop. The secretary was a priest. Other board members included four farmers, one lawyer and one civil engineer by professional training and one commercial radio station owner.

Initial Effect

Acquisition and expansion of the existing electric distribution system in Santo Domingo resulted in improved service for old consumers and the availability of service for new consumers. Some new businesses were established and old businesses converted their operations to take advantage of the 24-hour electric service.

Among the new or expanded industries and businesses were a new radio station, an ice manufacturing plant, a bottling plant, a new garage, a spaghetti factory, a coffee and cocoa processing plant, a banana packaging plant, a 30-room hotel, a sawmill, a meat storage plant as well as 125 homes and small businesses.

The ice cream factory had been using two generators with capacities of 5 KW and 3 KW. The owner had computed the cost of energy at S/.1.50 per KWH for fuel and depreciation and amortization of the generators. Minimum monthly consumption was 2,500 while in some months consumption rose to 4,500 KWH. Monthly energy costs for the ice cream plant through electric service from the cooperative were reduced approximately 70 percent (see Table 105).

The ice cream plant was producing between 1,000 and 1,500 liters of ice cream monthly. In addition, it produced about 400 quintales (1 quintal equals 100 kilograms) of ice monthly. While the ice cream plant was enjoying a 70 percent savings in energy costs from electric service by the

TABLE 105

Monthly KWH Consumption and Cost of Energy from
the Cooperative Compared to the Cost of Power
from the Small Generators Used by the Ice
Cream Plant in Santo Domingo,
October, 1965

Mo. of Billing	KWH Consumption*	Cost from Coop. (in sucres)	Est. Cost for Private Generation	% Saved
April	4,325	1,828.50	6,487.50	72
May	2,530	1,294.40	3,795.00	66
June	2,933	1,299.60	4,399.50	68
July	2,851	1,268.40	4,276.50	70
Aug.	4,038	1,371.50	6,057.00	77
Sept.	2,990	1,361.20	4,485.00	70
Oct.	3,084	1,367.10	4,646.00	70
Average	3,250	1,398.67	4,875.21	71

*Computed on the basis of S/.1.50 per KWH.

Source: Cooperative and ice cream plant records.

cooperative, it also was being subjected to decreased sales. The owner of the ice cream plant
explained that several restaurants in Santo Domingo
had purchased ice cream-making machines since 24-
hour electric service had become available. Since
they were producing their own ice cream, his sales
had dropped. But despite the reduction in sales,
net profit for the ice cream plant had increased
substantially because of the decreased energy costs.

The owner of the ice cream plant cited four
advantages to service from the rural electric cooperative: (1) less cost for production, (2) labor
savings averaging two hours per day, (3) more reliable source of power and (4) it saved his "pa-
tience."

Many people in Santo Domingo were using electric irons since energization of the cooperative. Several had converted from kerosene refrigerators to electric refrigerators and some had purchased washing machines. There was also a pressing machine being used commercially. All these things made living more pleasant.

A vocational school was using electric power tools and shop equipment where it had none before. Three radio stations had expanded facilities and were broadcasting educational programs. The hospital had purchased an x-ray machine and was planning to purchase electric sterilizers. A Buffalo, New York, Catholic Youth Organization was donating $100,000 worth of hospital equipment. These changes would not have occurred without reliable 24-hour electric service. Thus, in the initial stages the rural electric cooperative had beneficial effects on health and education in Santo Domingo.

A new restaurant had opened where electric service had been made available. A water cooperative formed in a nearby colonization project that had requested electric service. There was no motive power in the area for obtaining water. In Daule, where a second rural electric cooperative had been formed using the pattern of the Santo Domingo Cooperative, community leaders were considering developing a water system based on the idea of the electric cooperative. The village was obtaining water from a nearby river.

It was the consensus that 5 of 14 leaders in the rural electric cooperative had assumed definite roles of individual leadership in the community after having been elected to their positions on the board of directors and the vigilance committee. These 5 men had become leaders in developing community projects such as paving the streets, trying to improve the local school, attempting to obtain legislation to make Santo Domingo a county rather than a township, working for a better water supply and trying to improve sewage facilities.

Rural electrification had created jobs in Santo Domingo with the expansion of old businesses and development of new businesses. The cooperative itself had a staff of 15 where the old distribution system was only employing 3 people. Since electricity had not reached the farms, there was no effect on labor in agriculture.

These are some of the effects of the rural electric cooperative on Santo Domingo. As the distribution system is extended to the rural areas the benefits should increase. Not all of the effects of cooperative rural electrification in Santo Domingo have been beneficial to certain individuals, but the effects have been favorable to development of the community.

Problems and Progress

The most significant problem confronting the cooperative during its first 18 months of operation was the delay in implementing the loan and, consequently, the delay in construction of the system. This delay in construction was possibly the cause of other problems including functioning of the board of directors.

During the first 18 months of operation, the original manager of the cooperative left Santo Domingo to accept a position in Quito. Since the manager of the cooperative had to be approved by the AID Mission in Quito as well as INECEL, there was considerable discussion and disagreement about hiring a new manager. Some doubted that dental training was a satisfactory background for becoming manager of a rural electric cooperative. But the new manager was hired on a temporary basis which became "more or less" permanent.

A special problem of the board was their lack of ability to carry out business. The board met every Tuesday night and most of the meetings lasted until after midnight, but the time was spent in discussing and debating an issue. It was reported that the board was extremely hesitant to make a decision.

Two special problems that were bound to have a detrimental effect on operations of the cooperative in the future were the high cost of connection for electric service per consumer and the fact that the industrial rate was lower than the cost of generating power. A consensus of possible problem areas is shown in Table 106.

When the cooperative began operations there were 164 consumers per kilometer of primary distribution line. By expanding the system to 17.5 kilometers of line it permitted 240 more homes and businesses to receive electric service. However, it reduced the number of consumers per kilometer of line by 78 percent (see Table 107). At the same time this decreased density increased the cost of operations.

TABLE 106

Consensus of Possible Problem Areas in the
Santo Domingo Rural Electric Cooperative,
October, 1965

Possible Problem Area	Yes	No	Comment
Idle services	-	X	--
Minimum bill users	-	X	Anticipated
Peak demands	X	-	--
Utilizing system capacity	X	-	Daytime only
Adequate power supply	X	-	--
Technical operations	-	X	--
Maintenance	-	X	--
Board relations	X	-	--
Community relations	-	X	--
Voltage regulation	-	X	--
Consumer complaints	-	X	--
Equipment availability	X	-	Lack meter tester
Equipment servicing	X	-	Lack parts
Farm wiring	-	X	Not started
Load factor	X	-	--
Outages	-	X	--
Lack of member interest	X	-	No service

Source: AID and INECEL advisors.

TABLE 107

Progress Report on Operating Data and Related Factors in the Santo Domingo
Rural Electric Cooperative, October, 1965

Item	Unit	Month of Energization	Time after Energization		
			6 Mos.	12 Mos.	18 Mos.
Consumers	No.	374	560	614	646
Meters connected	No.	350	560	614	646
Membership	No.	400	736	815	963
Power generation	KWH	25,401	86,000	83,756	--
Power consumption	KWH	20,000	63,248	59,681	62,863
Energy lost	%				
Per capita consumption	KWH	53	119	97	97
Meters disconnected	No.	--	--	38	40
Delinquent bills	No.	--	47	38	46
Delinquent payments	Sucres	--	5,800	10,000	23,300
Cost of power	Sucres	--	--	--	--
Energy sales	Sucres	18,500	50,095	50,834	55,784
Primary lines	Kms.	2.28	--	17.5	--
Village	Kms.	2.28	--	17.5	--
Rural	Kms.	--	--	--	--

(Continued)

TABLE 107 (Continued)

Item	Unit	Month of Energization	Time after Energization		
			6 Mos.	12 Mos.	18 Mos.
Consumers per Km. of line					
Village	No.	164	--	35	--
Rural	No.	164	--	35	--
	No.	--	--	--	--
Cost of Appliances:					
Iron (minimum)	Sucres	--	--	--	450
Iron (maximum)	Sucres	--	--	--	1,200
Radio (minimum)	Sucres	--	--	--	1,000
Motor (1/2 HP)	Sucres	--	--	--	1,200
Motor (1 HP)	Sucres	--	--	--	1,500
Motor (3 HP)	Sucres	--	--	--	2,200
Television	Sucres	--	--	--	2,500
Refrigerator (3 cu. ft.)	Sucres	--	--	--	4,000
Refrigerator (6 cu. ft.)	Sucres	--	--	--	6,500
Hot plate	Sucres	--	--	--	100
Toaster	Sucres	--	--	--	450
Water pump (1/2 HP)	Sucres	--	--	--	2,000
Deep freeze (6 cu. ft.)	Sucres	--	--	--	12,000

Source: Cooperative records and field survey.

246

During the first year of operation the cooperative showed a net loss of S/.33,183.96, or
$1,843.55. However, receipts from membership fees
of S/.40,610.00 were not included as income. This
was primarily because membership fees were nonre-
fundable. Including the membership fees as income
to the cooperative would have produced net margins
to the cooperative of S/.7,426.04, or about $412.56.

Expenses during the first year of operation
were higher than normal due to: (1) overhauling of
two generators, (2) extensive maintenance required
on the distribution system, (3) training of personnel, (4) lack of equipment and tools, (5) rate
schedule not adequate to cover operations, (6) cost
of organization and (7) cost of member surveys.

To rectify some of these problems the retail
rates were increased 8 percent on April 1, 1965.
With the increased rate and through improved management it was anticipated that operating losses
would be reduced during the second year of operation. Also, when more efficient generators were
placed in operation, generating costs would be lowered. Line losses also would be decreased when a
new system replaced the existing system. General
overhead expenses were not expected to increase
significantly when the system was expanded to include the rural areas; therefore, the cooperative
would benefit as a result of economy of scale.

FIVE YEARS AFTER ENERGIZATION

Phase A of the construction plan for new distribution lines was completed in 1967.[1] It consisted of the construction of public lighting and
distribution networks for the urban area. Extension of these lines in 1969 consisted of 12.5 kilometers of high voltage, 14 kilometers of low voltage
and 13.3 kilometers of public lighting. Phase B,
completed in 1968, provided electricity to the rural areas adjacent to the four highways that meet
in Santo Domingo. These lines, in 1969, consisted

of 134.0 kilometers of high voltage, 6.5 kilometers
of low voltage and 6.5 kilometers of public lighting.

After completing construction of Phases A and
B using AID loan funds, the cooperative expanded
rural distribution using its own financial resources. As of October, 1969, the power lines provided as a result of this expansion consisted of
34.3 kilometers of high voltage, 3.3 kilometers of
low voltage and 3.3 kilometers of public lighting.

Membership and Consumption

In March, 1964, when the cooperative first
started operation, it had 374 consumers in the urban area and none in the rural area. During the
early feasibility studies it was estimated that by
the end of 1973 membership of the cooperative would
be divided equally between the urban and rural
areas, at about 2,000 each. By October, 1969, the
actual distribution of membership was 1,272 in the
urban area and 458 in the rural area for a total of
1,730. Annual growth in membership and consumption
of electricity are shown in Table 108.

TABLE 108

Number of Consumers, Kilowatt-Hours Consumed and
Average Annual Consumption per Member, 1964-69

Year	No. of Consumers	KWH Consumed	Ave. Consumption per Member in KWH
1964	470	323,503	69
1965	625	741,183	119
1966	732	975,911	132
1967	863	1,592,121	184
1968	1,190	2,549,614	214
1969*	1,730	2,181,130	133

*Figures for 1969 are through August 31 only.

Source: Cooperative records.

At the start of its operations the cooperative possessed only two generators with a combined capacity of 300 kilowatts. It was estimated at that time that the three donated war surplus generators, having a combined capacity of 1,380 kilowatts would suffice to meet the demand for electric power until 1974. This estimate was inaccurate. In October, 1969, the total capacity of the three generators was already needed to meet the current demand, and the cooperative was having problems with sudden drops in the voltage during the peak hours of power consumption. Thus, by 1970 the cooperative had to install another generator with a capacity of 1,100 kilowatts and in 1973 yet another with the same capacity will be needed.

From a commercial point of view the cooperative is a business concern composed of shareholders, a board of directors and a managerial staff. All of the shareholders are users of the electric power furnished by the cooperative. Each share is worth S/.100 and cannot be transferred from one member to another without the board of directors' authorization. The number of shares held by each member is proportionate to the amount of electric power that he uses. As of mid-October, 1969, the cooperative had issued 7,660 shares having a total value of S/.766,000 and representing the cooperative's major source of working capital.

Other sources of working capital were: (1) the admission fees that amount to S/.50 a member and are not refundable (2) the goods and chattels of the cooperative, (3) the loans, donations and subsidies that the cooperative may succeed in obtaining from persons or entities and (4) the legally required reserve funds, funds for education and any other funds that might be established for specific purposes.

Bylaws of the cooperative call for a general meeting of the shareholders twice a year in January and June. Special meetings are held whenever necessary. At the general meetings the reports by the

board of directors are approved, appeals are considered and the general policy of the organization
is set.

The board of directors, consisting of nine
members elected by vote, meets once a week and is
responsible, through the manager, for the administration of the cooperative. The board of directors
contracts the services of the manager who super-
vises the work of the cooperative's other employees.
In October, 1969, the cooperative had 34 employees,
compared to 15 in October, 1965.

Status of the cooperative's accounts and fi-
nances as of August, 1969, showed assets amounting
to S/.23,524,939 and liabilities amounting to
S/.15,260,054; it thus appeared that within five
years after energization the cooperative had accumulated capital amounting to S/.8,264,885. In this
amount, however, is included the estimated value of
donations (S/.4,055,300) such as all of the generators, the equipment donated by the Kentucky Rural
Electric Cooperative Corporation, land for the
building of a substation and technical assistance
provided by INECEL.

The cooperative's "surplus statement" for the
month of August, 1969, indicated that the net operating income from January to August, 1969, was
S/.30,432. This amount divided by eight months
indicated an average monthly profit for 1969 of
S/.3,804.

The cooperative's "real profit" does not ap-
pear in any balance sheet as such. There are two
reasons for this: (1) it is the only source for
increasing and expanding services, (2) it is a
method of avoiding the recording of large profits
that would make the cooperative liable for the payment of high legal contributions (not taxes) and
also would indicate a surplus of considerable value
that the shareholders could demand as dividends for
themselves, thus impeding the expansion of the cooperative's service.

A clearer picture of the profits can be obtained from an analysis of the production cost of a
kilowatt and the difference between that and its
sale price, but in the electrification cooperative
of Santo Domingo this is not possible, once again
because the profits are reinvested and are not
shown as reinvestments in the balance sheet.

In the month of June, 1969, for example, the
total cost of operations was S/.214,198, and the
number of kilowatts sold was 229,640. The total
cost of operations divided by the total number of
kilowatts sold reveals that the cost of a kilowatt-
hour was S/.0.93.

The average sale price of a kilowatt-hour was
S/.0.85 on each kilowatt. Nevertheless the cooperative assumes responsibility for the cost of new
constructions and new equipment of higher generating capacity, has a sizable reserve in the "Bank
Accounts" ("Bancos") category, and in the difference between its assets and its liabilities there
was a favorable balance of over S/.4 million.

Management

The cooperative's administrative council holds
a meeting every Thursday to discuss only what is on
the agenda. The manager informs the nine council
members of his work and the developments of the
past week, and receives from them whatever authori-
zations and instructions he may need for the following week.

Each member of the administrative council
serves for a term of three years, but every year at
the general assembly of the cooperative's members
three new members of the council are elected.

The cooperative's supervisory council meets
once a month, and on specific occasions holds a
joint meeting with the administrative council.
Once a year two of its five members are replaced by
election during the general assembly of the cooperative's members.

The cooperative's manager is accountable to the supervisory council and to an auditor of INECEL for his activities, which consist of administering the cooperative's affairs and directing the construction and maintenance work. In October, 1969, the manager was an electrical engineer from INECEL.

The extent to which the ordinary members of the cooperative take an active interest in the management of its affairs may be judged by their actions at the general meetings of the cooperative's entire membership. An observer from the AID Mission to Ecuador attended a special meeting of the general assembly on October 15, 1969, and provided the following comments:

> Only 286 of the total 1,736 members of the cooperative attended the meeting, i.e., 16 percent, and all those who attended were from the urban area. The fact that the general meetings are held at night produces a transportation problem for the rural members of the cooperative, and prevents their attendance.
>   Members having no grievances against the cooperative, its services and its management did not attend the meeting. All members present had personal or, more often, political reasons, for taking the cooperative's board of directors to task. In these circumstances the decisions reached at the meeting could not be altogether constructive and impartial. The cooperative's board of directors and its manager were on the defensive, realizing that however wise and beneficial their actions may have been, they were still subject to the criticism of the dissatisfied members attending the meeting. Their interest in doing better work in order to reduce the complaints and criticisms

can, of course, be advantageous for
the cooperative as a whole.

The observer noted

that the cooperative's supervisory
committee does not yet seem to have
a clear understanding of the principles which originally led to its
creation. It is supposed to watch
over the actions of the board of directors as well as to make sure that
the obligations and duties of the
general membership are accomplished.
In practice, however, it assumes a
police-like attitude towards the cooperative's administrative staff. At
present all of the members of the supervisory committee belong to the
same political party and function
mainly in terms of their own interest
or the interest of the party.
     Santo Domingo is a place to
which people from other parts of the
country continually go to settle.
Among the newcomers there is a strong
tendency to take the place of the
people who have been there longest,
and those, naturally, react by trying
to retain their place. In the cooperative the dissatisfied members and
those who stir up doubts and distrust
are the newcomers. Members who have
been in Santo Domingo for over six
months are satisfied with the electric
service and the cooperative's actions
because most of them remember the
situation that existed before the cooperative was formed and realize the
significant change which the cooperative's work has produced in the place.
     An inadequate understanding of
the basic principles of the cooperative system characterizes the general

membership of the Santo Domingo electrification cooperative. The board
of directors realizes this, and is
studying ways and means of familiar-
izing the public with the cooperative's work and the concept of co-
operativism.

The board of directors would also
like to set up a new system for the
general meetings, one in which the
people in each section or district of
the area would elect a given number
of members to represent them at the
general meetings and act on their be-
half. Such a system, however, cannot
be put into effect unless it is approved at a general meeting.

In spite of the problems which
the cooperative has faced, the majority of its members regard it favorably,
and take pride in its accomplishments,
which are also theirs, even though
their understanding of this fact is
sometimes hazy. The chief complaint
among them is about the <u>cost of electricity, which is relatively high because the power is generated thermal-
ly</u>. The prevailing attitude of the
consumers who do not attend the cooperative's general meetings is that
their participation in these meetings
is not needed since the cooperative is
functioning very well.[2]

Effect on Growth

Santo Domingo's progress in recent years has
been chiefly of a commercial nature. Hotels, restaurants, bars and shops of numerous sorts have
sprung up there, and most of them stay open at
night. There is now a substantial tourist trade in
Santo Domingo that might not have developed on the
same scale if hotels had found it necessary to purchase their own generators. Also it is possible

that the local business of bars, restaurants and
shops has increased as a result of electrification.

Industry in the Santo Domingo area is a recent
development, but by 1969 it had already acquired
some importance. FRESCA, a meat packing industry,
employed 38 people and consumed 169,863 kilowatt-
hours of electric power. There were in the area,
several sawmills, ice plants, canneries, bottling
plants and grain-processing plants. Their existence
was to a great extent the result of the electric
power service made available by the cooperative.

Industry's importance in the Santo Domingo
area, however, will be impeded as long as certain
situations such as the following prevail there.
Many industry owners, especially in the rural sections, installed their own generators before the
cooperative made public electricity available.
These generators are still relatively new and provide the industry owners with good service; so they
are reluctant to change their source of power. For
the most part these people use the cooperative's
electricity for their houses and their own equipment for their industries. The cost of electric
power also has a negative effect, at least in the
minds of the consumers. Actually the cost of electricity for industry in Santo Domingo in 1969 was
the same as it is throughout the country, i.e.,
S/.0.45 per kilowatt-hour, which compared to the
cost of S/.0.90 per kilowatt-hour for private residences and the cost of up to S/.1.15 per kilowatt-
hour for business. Uninformed of the cost of electricity in other parts of Ecuador, many owners of
industries in the Santo Domingo area who could become consumers of the electric power provided by
the cooperative hesitated to do so because they
considered its cost too high.

The importance of the influence of electric
power in Santo Domingo was surveyed in the AID
study in terms of the four categories into which it
is divided for sales purposes: residential, commercial, industrial and public.

1. Residential--Both the town and the rural
area had electric power for private residences. As
a result, residents were able to use many household
appliances, which raised their standard of living.

2. Commercial--As mentioned previously, business has been the major cause of development in
Santo Domingo, especially business related to tour-
ism. Two first-class hotels in the town were pros-
pering. Without electricity they could not be operated, although they might,of course, have been
constructed, and might have attracted tourists even
if a communal source of electricity were not available. The owners, however, would have had to install their own generators.

3. Industrial--Industries will become more
important consumers of electric power when conver-
sion to the hydroelectric system of power generation comes into being and power costs are reduced.
The cooperative's officers are trying to find the
best way of reaching this solution expeditiously.

4. Public--The cooperative spends most of its
time and money on public lighting, mainly because
of the area's constant growth. The town has doubled in size within five years, and its expansion
in all directions continues. Investment in public
lighting, however, has so far represented a loss to
the cooperative. The municipality, although
obliged by law to pay for electricity, does not re-
imburse the cooperative. The municipality's accumulated indebtedness to the cooperative for street
lights in October, 1969, was S/.381,994. The rate
charged for public lighting, S/.0.35 per kilowatt-
hour, was the lowest of all and represented only
about half of the actual cost of generation. Although the cooperative had approached the municipality many times about this matter, it had not
obtained any results.

Contribution of AID Loans

Three factors are usually taken into account
where analysis of the effects of an AID loan are

concerned: (1) the local contribution, (2) donations and (3) the loan.

The local contribution consisted of
the value of the members' contribution certificates, totalling S/.766,000,
and the contribution by the Municipality of Quito of the cooperative's
original generating system, i.e., two
150 kilowatt Caterpillar generators
and the distribution network in the
town.

With only these resources the
cooperative's development would have
been very slow and difficult. The
cooperative would have been unable to
meet the growing demand for electric
power, and thus would have caused the
national government one more unsolved
problem.

In addition to these resources,
donations valued at S/.4,055,300 put
the cooperative in a better position.
These donations would have enabled
the cooperative to provide service to
most of the town although not in the
expanse that the town had reached by
1969. Without the loan, however, the
cooperative would have had to finance
on its own such necessities as the
building for the machinery, the substation, and other works for which
the loan was used.

The AID loan was used principally for rural electrification, or
phase B of the cooperative's program.
Each kilometer of transmission lines
costs S/.40,000 on the average. The
loan made possible the construction
of 140 kilometers of lines. The ap-
proximate cost of phase B was S/.5.6
million, a bill which could not have
been paid through local means.

In short, the loan turned the
cooperative into a large business and

multiplied its growth potential pro-
portionately. Without the loan the
cooperative would have remained a
small organization with a low income
and few possibilities for expansion.
The loan facilitated the formation of
a strong, financially self-sufficient
organization capable of undertaking
considerable investments on its own
initiative, an organization which has
been able to keep up with the demand
for electric power in the fastest
growing area of the country, and which
has so far completed at its own expense, 34 kilometers of transmission
lines in the expansion of phase B of
its program, at a cost of S/.40,000
per kilometer.[3]

To meet the growing demand for electricity,
the cooperative contracted for a new generator,
valued at $150,000, having a capacity of 1,100
kilowatts.

NOTES

1. Information presented in this section was
obtained from Report No. 2, prepared by the Evaluation Section of the Office of Program Planning, AID
Mission to Ecuador. The report was approved by the
USAID/E Evaluation Committee on February 27, 1970.

2. Ibid., pp. 36-38.

3. Ibid., pp. 42-43.

5

NICARAGUA:
ELECTRIFICATION
AND
RURAL
MODERNIZATION

Nicaragua is about the size of the state of
Louisiana and is the largest of the Central American republics. Its population of 1.8 million in
1968 was about the same as that of Nebraska.

The most striking natural features of Nicaragua are a chain of volcanoes paralleling its Pacific coast, and two large bodies of water, Lake Nicaragua and Lake Managua. A low mountain range to
the east of the two lakes divides the country into
two distinct regions. Between this mountain range
and the Pacific Ocean lies the Pacific region.
Most of the country's population and economic activity are located in this area which is 50 to 100
miles wide. To the east of the mountain range lies
the Atlantic region where heavy rainfall, jungles
and pests have prevented settlement and have frus-
trated attempts to develop commercial agriculture.

STRUCTURE OF THE RURAL ECONOMY

Agriculture is the most important sector of
Nicaragua's economy. There are small manufacturing
enterprises and mining, forestry and shrimp fishing

offer promising possibilities. But within the near
future, agriculture will be the major factor in the
country's development.

Agriculture accounts for approximately 35 percent of Nicaragua's GNP and for 85 percent of all
exports. Nearly 60 percent of Nicaragua's population is rural and dependent upon agriculture. In
addition, many more people in the urban areas are
concerned with processing and marketing of agricultural products. This points out that not only the
productive capacity of the nation but also the internal consumption potential is determined largely
by the well being of the agricultural sector.

Prosperity or recession in Nicaragua's economy
depends upon markets abroad for agricultural products. For many years gold was the country's principal export. Even today in the eastern jungle
areas, gold is still the major industry. Silver
and copper are also mined to a certain extent in
conjunction with gold. Lumbering was an important
industry on the Atlantic Coast, but depletion of
the easily accessible forests has caused a sharp
decline in this industry. Shrimp and lobster fishing on both coasts is growing in importance and
several plants freeze these products for export.

The country is in an early stage of industrialization. Manufacturing consists primarily of
processed foods, beverages, cigarettes, textiles,
soap and building materials. Industry is now expanding steadily and is becoming more diversified.
The government is trying to encourage new investment in industry.

Nicaragua is a member of the Central American
Common Market and is beginning to integrate its
economy with those of Guatemala, Honduras, El Sal-
vador and Costa Rica. Free trade among these countries in most items already exists and external
tariffs on many items have been equalized. Since
the Common Market area will offer a much larger
market than that represented by individual

countries it is likely that many manufacturing industries will be established that would not otherwise be attracted.

Nicaragua has been making substantial progress
in improving its highway system. Good paved roads
now connect the principal centers of economic activity in the Pacific region of the country and an all-
weather road has been built to connect the Pacific
region with the Atlantic region. A government-
owned railroad provides transportation from the
port of Corinto to the principal cities of the Pacific region. Nicaragua also has an airline and a
steamship line.

Electric power capacity has recently been doubled by the development of hydroelectric power on
the Tuma River in the northern part of the country.
This project, which provides an installed capacity
of 50,000 KW, was completed in 1965. Similar hydroelectric projects are in the planning stage.

The unit of monetary exchange in Nicaragua is
the cordoba, which is freely convertible with the
dollar at the rate of C $7.00 for U.S. $1.00.

Approximately 20 percent of the total land
area, or 7.3 million acres, is used for farming.
Of the 7.3 million acres, 12 percent is in annual
crops, 6 percent in permanent crops, 12 percent
fallow, 47 percent in pasture and 23 percent unused. Forests are estimated to cover 17.5 million
acres.

Commercial agriculture in Nicaragua is in the
hands of a relatively small number of farmers.
Less than 2 percent of the landowners control more
than 40 percent of the farming area. Farms of 87
acres or less account for nearly 75 percent of the
total number of farms.

Commercial farmers are operating at a reason-
ably high level of efficiency and economic returns.
The smaller farmers represent a great source of

potential development, but this source can only be
utilized by an initial investment of the government
in extension, education and research, provision of
credit, rural electrification, and associated
agrarian reform activities.

Agricultural production is continuing to expand in Nicaragua as a result of the rapid growth
of export crops--cotton, sugar, coffee and beef.
However, food crops are not developing fast enough
to keep up with local demand.

Corn is the major food crop, but production in
recent years has not been enough to make the country self-sufficient. Imports have been primarily
from the United States.

Rice and beans are other important food crops.
Rice production has been declining because of dis-
ease problems, low yields resulting from poor cultural methods and competition for the land from
cotton. Rice imports from the United States have
been increasing to meet the local demand. Bean
production has increased slightly but not enough to
keep even with the population increase.

The cotton industry is continuing to expand
rapidly and is one of the main factors causing the
rapid rise in Nicaragua's economic activity since
1961. Lint cotton production in the country increased about 90 percent during the first five
years of the 1960's. The rate of growth has been
stimulated almost entirely by the favorable world
market. Japan and West Germany are Nicaragua's
best cotton customers.

Agricultural exports account for the bulk of
Nicagarua's foreign exchange earnings. Cotton is
by far the most important export item accounting
for nearly 40 percent of the total earnings in recent years. Coffee is the next most important foreign exchange earner, accounting for about 15 percent of the total. Meat, sugar and cottonseed are

the next most important agricultural export items
accounting for another 20 percent of the country's
exchange earnings. Banana exports have become more
important recently with efforts to revive the country's banana industry. Other important agricultural exports are sesame, cattle and cacao beans.

Agricultural products represent only a small
share of the total import value. Wheat flour, rice,
leaf tobacco, fruits and preparations, and vegetables and preparations are the principal items.

Nicaragua, along with mother Latin American
countries, has shown increased interest in recent
years in rural development. Specific development
projects have been sponsored by the government and
an Agrarian Reform Law was enacted in 1963.

Agrarian reform is probably the most important
development program that has been instituted in
Nicaragua. The program is moving ahead slowly with
most of the progress being made in the area of land
titles. The policy of the Land Reform Institute
has been to keep colonization projects to a minimum
and concentrate on titles and parcelization programs.

SOCIOECONOMIC CONDITIONS IN
THE PROJECT AREA

The Tisma Rural Electric Cooperative area is
located approximately 20 kilometers southeast of
Managua, the capital of Nicaragua. It covers an
agricultural area of 115 square miles and includes
an estimated population of 10,000. While the legal
name of the cooperative is Cooperativa de Abastecimiento de Energia Electrica Rural No. 1, it is
more popularly known as the Tisma Rural Electric
Cooperative. This has come about because the village of Tisma has the largest population concentra-
tion in the cooperative area.

Geography and Climate

The cooperative area consists of the Municipio of Tisma, almost all of the rural area of the Municipio of Masaya and a small portion of the Department of Managua. Since the Municipio of Tisma is the only political and administrative entity entirely included in the cooperative area, the study was concentrated on Tisma--the village itself and the rural area in the Municipio of Tisma.

Tisma, a thatched and tiled roof village of 242 houses, is located 30 kilometers east-southeast of Managua and 18 kilometers northwest of Granada. The village is the administrative headquarters for the Municipio of Tisma. The Tisma Rural Electric Cooperative covers an area of wide valleys and plains. It is a level area and the soils are productive. The water table on the average varies from 10 to 15 feet below ground surface.

Population and Education

According to the 1963 census there were 3,828 people living in the Municipio of Tisma. Of the total, 1,377 were urban and 2,451 were rural. A comparison of the 1950 census with that of 1963 shows that the village population of Tisma increased from 791 to 1,377 but the total population of the Municipio decreased from 4,145 to 3,828. Thus, the rural population of the Municipio of Tisma declined 27 percent from 1950 to 1963. During the Community Survey on April 7, 1965, it was estimated by the Police Judge of Tisma that the population of the village was continuing to increase. He said the population was moving into the village because they expected an agricultural processing plant to be built after electric lines were extended to Tisma.

The Police Judge also estimated that 25 percent of the population could read and write. According to the 1950 census, the level of literacy in the Department of Masaya (roughly applicable to the

cooperative area) was 50 percent for the urban
areas and 20 percent for the rural areas. The average was 33 percent, compared to 38 percent for
the entire country.

This indicates that the level of literacy of
the rural electric cooperative area in 1950 was approximately 20 percent. According to the 1963 census there was a 12.7 percent increase over 1950 of
the percentage of the population attending grade
school. Therefore, the estimate of 25 percent literacy in Tisma seems quite reasonable. About 50
percent of Nicaragua's total population in 1963 was
classified as literate.

The only school in Tisma at the time of the
field study was called Benjamin Zeledon. It was a
six-year school with 204 students and 6 teachers,
including the director of the school. The school
building, constructed in 1958 by the National Government, had four classrooms. Corridors were also
used for classrooms according to the director.
Salaries of the teachers were paid by the National
Government.

Of the ten consumers interviewed in Tisma only
two thought the local school was well managed.
When the director of the school was interviewed, he
said the parents were uncooperative. There was no
parent-teacher organization. Meetings with the
parents had been scheduled, according to the director, but the parents failed to attend the meetings.
And there was no program for adult education.

Community Welfare and Leadership

The community of Tisma consisted of 242 houses
and 1,377 people, with an average of 5.8 persons
living in each house. The typical home had one
room; it was used for everything except cooking
(the kitchen was located outside the house). In
the rural areas of Tisma there were 389 houses and
a population of 2,451, with an average of 6.3 persons per house. These, also, were primarily one-
room houses.

It was estimated by the Police Judge that 50 percent of the houses had thatched roofs and 50 percent had tiled roofs. Approximately 75 percent had dirt floors, 20 percent wooden and 5 percent concrete. The majority did not have enclosed walls. Of the houses, 20 percent had wooden walls and 10 percent had brick walls.

During the five years prior to the study, at least three houses with thatched roofs had burned. Kerosene lamps ignited the thatched roofs and caused the fires.

There were no community facilities for drainage in Tisma. Each house also had to provide its own water supply. In some cases dwellers in a group of houses agreed to share an open well, practically the only method of obtaining water.

There were no doctors, dentists, nurses or pharmacists in Tisma. Most of the people who could afford medical and dental care went to Masaya, approximately 20 kilometers from Tisma. There were 15 midwives in Tisma but all of them were without a license. The nearest health clinic was in Masaya.

The only organization in the community was called Union de Pequenas Agricultores, an association of small farmers. It was being promoted by the extension service in Masaya and Managua. Plans called for the organization to develop into an agricultural cooperative, concerned with both production and marketing.

Community leaders in Tisma included the Mayor and the Police Judge. The Mayor was Mrs. Yelba de Urbina. She was a dressmaker by trade but also instrumental in operating her father's farm near Tisma. She completed eight years of school and her main desire in life is to move to some other area.

Transportation and Communication

The major means of transportation from Tisma to market was by truck, jeep or small bus. Horses

were often used for personal transportation and ox
carts were used to transport materials and products
locally.

The main road entering Tisma was gravel; however, the streets in Tisma were primarily dirt and
during the rainy season these roads often became
impassable. There also were paths entering Tisma
that were used by people walking or riding horseback.

The cost of riding a bus from Tisma to Managua
one-way was C $3.00 per person. The price for
transporting one box of tomatoes was C $1.00. A
farmer taking one box of tomatoes to the market in
Managua and returning to Tisma had to pay C $7.00,
6 for the round trip for himself and 1 for his tomatoes. This was equivalent to one day's wages for
an agricultural worker.

There was a mail system in Tisma plus post,
telephone and telegraph offices. Radio and television reception in the community were considered
good.

Employment and Wages

According to the 1950 census, slightly less
than 30 percent of the rural population were economically active and about 31 percent of the urban
population were economically active in the Department of Masaya. Considering 30 percent of Tisma's
population as being economically active gives a
working force of 413 men and women in Tisma and 735
in the rural areas of the Municipio. The census
shows that approximately 55 percent of the male
population were economically active while only 3.5
percent of the female population earned an income.

Of the 413 workers in the village of Tisma,
70 percent were employed directly in agriculture.
Indirectly, the village relied 100 percent on agriculture. Services employed the next largest group,
18 percent. Employment of Tisma's labor force was
as shown in Table 109.

TABLE 109

Number of Workers and Type of Employment
in Tisma, 1965

Type of Employment	No. of Establishments	No. of Workers	% of Workers
General stores	8	24	6
Canteens	12	36	9
Shoemakers	2	2	-
Dressmakers	5	5	1
Barbers	5	5	1
Bakeries	4	8	1
Fishing	-	50	12
Agriculture	-	293	70
Total:		423	100

Source: Community Survey.

Picking cotton was one of the largest areas of
employment of the agricultural workers. This oc-
curred from January through March. The workers
were paid from C $6 to C $8 for picking one quintal
of cotton. One worker could pick about 1.5 quintals
a day. In April the workers were employed in shell-
ing corn and cleaning the farm areas. From May to
October they worked in planting, cultivating and
harvesting corn. For this work they received C $6
a day. From November to May they worked in the
tomato fields and received from C $7 to C $8 a day.

Production and Marketing

Cotton, tomatoes, corn and sesame were the
principal cash crops in the Tisma area. Corn, rice,
yuca and milk were the most important food products.

According to information for the 1951-52 agricultural year, the latest census data available,
there were 241 farms covering 10,657 manzanas (a

manzana is equal to 1.736 acres) in the Municipio of Tisma.

Marketing of products from the Tisma area was handled almost entirely by trucks. Some of the smaller farmers transported their products by ox cart to Masaya. The principal markets, however, were Managua and Granda. The truck route from Tisma to Managua was 40 kilometers and from Tisma to Granada it was 50 kilometers.

Cotton from the Tisma area was sold both in Managua and Granada. The market price varied considerably but was roughly C $60 per quintal. Corn was sold primarily in Managua. The price was approximately C $10 for one box and a box weighed roughly 35 pounds. Milk was sold in Managua and Masaya. The price in Masaya varied from C $2 to C $4 for one gallon, while the Managua market paid C $2 per gallon. It was estimated that from 20 to 30 cows were sold for meat every week from the Tisma area. Both Masaya and Managua were important meat markets. Sesame was sold at C $60 per quintal, primarily in Granada.

Transportation costs of marketing milk from Tisma to Managua were approximately C $2.50 for 10 gallons. In addition, the producer had to pay C $0.20 per gallon for cooling the milk.

Some of the agricultural products were marketed in Tisma, but the local market was limited. Markets in order of importance were Managua, Masaya and Granada.

Income, Savings and Investment

Typical income for a family working as farm laborers was about C $70 per week. If the family workers were employed every week during the year, the family's annual income would be C $3,640. At C $7 per $1, the annual family income could be as high as $520. This was estimated on the basis of 1.8 workers per family. On the basis of 5.8

members per family, annual per capita income was
about $90.

Investigations carried out in 1961 in the cooperative area showed that the lowest family income
on the average was C $12.00 ($1.71) a day. It was
estimated that about 25 percent of the families in
the cooperative area were in this category. The
average family income of the initial members of the
cooperative was about C $20 ($2.86) a day. This
did not include the large-load consumers. In general, all families in addition to their cash incomes received from C $6 to C $9 worth of food a
day from their employer.

The typical family debt was approximately
C $18.00 per week. This was the amount of the bill
charged at one of the general stores. Savings in
the area, except by the larger landowners and businessmen, was nonexistent. It was estimated that
there could be nominal savings in the average families, but any excess income above subsistence was
spent on alcoholic beverages.

There were no financial institutions in the
area. Among 242 families in the village of Tisma
only five had bank accounts. Investments were made
only by the larger landowners. Their savings usually were invested in additional land.

Electric Energy and Fuel Availability

There were five private generating plants operating in Tisma prior to operation of the rural
electric cooperative. Two were used in stores and
three were for residential use. Most of them operated about three hours in the evenings. Four of
the five plants had been purchased during the four
years prior to energization of the cooperative.
The size of each plant was approximately one kilowatt.

Several kinds of fuel were available in Tisma
at the general stores. The fuels and their prices

per gallon were: gasoline, C $3.00; kerosene,
C $2.00; diesel fuel, C $1.65; oil, C $16.00; and
coal, C $1.00.

DEVELOPMENT OF THE COOPERATIVE

In 1961 the Government of Nicaragua decided to
begin a program to electrify the agricultural areas
of the country with a pilot rural electric cooperative.   In its loan application, the National Energy
Commission stated, "After studying the socioeconomic
conditions of the rural population, it was decided
that the best method to electrify these areas would
be through the organization of cooperatives."   The
idea of starting with a pilot project was to "obtain information and experience."

Initial Investigation

In September, 1961, the USOM (United States
Overseas Mission) in Nicaragua contracted with Earl
J. Smith, a retired REA (Rural Electrification Administration) fieldman, as a "consultant in training
and planning for a rural electric cooperative."   His
tour of duty was 14 weeks.

At the time the request for assistance was
made to the USOM by the Government of Nicaragua, it
was anticipated that the National Power and Light
Company would sponsor the cooperative.   However, it
was later decided that the National Energy Commission would sponsor the cooperative and that the National Power and Light Company would supply wholesale electric power.

The National Power and Light Company is an
autonomous government-owned institution.   Purchasing electric energy from the company rather than
the cooperative producing power itself seemed more
feasible.   It lowered the initial investment, wholesale rates would be lower than what the cooperative
could produce for itself and the cooperative did
not have sufficiently trained personnel to operate
a generating plant.

Smith's recommendations included proceeding with the pilot project in the Tisma area and for the United States to provide assistance in the following areas: operations, training personnel, accounting, power use program and the encouragement of irrigation and industrialization.

Engineering Aspects

Wilfred C. Mast, manager of a rural electric cooperative and an electrical engineer, was employed by the AID Mission to Nicaragua in April, 1962, to make a ten-week study of engineering aspects of the project and to complete organization of the cooperative.

Maps of the cooperative area were prepared by the Civil Engineering Department of the National Energy Commission. From these maps line distances were measured and cost estimates were made. Using the standard REA method, a voltage drop study was prepared for the entire system. This study was used to determine wire size and loan balance. The system was designed to carry the power load for 10 years on the basis that the load would double every five years.

Following is a description of engineering aspects:

Primary Line--
      7.6/13.2 KV Grounded Wye
      77.1 miles single-phase 7.6 KV
      2.8 miles V-phase 7.6/13.2 KV
      33.7 miles three-phase 7.6/13.2 KV

Secondary and Service Line--
      Single-phase - 115/230 volts
      three-phase - 230 volts
      37.2 miles - 115/230 volts

Primary conductor--#4 6/1ACSR (Aluminum Cable Steel
      Reinforced)

Secondary conductor--#6 copper

Transformers--Conventional

Protective Equipment--Reclosers, sectionalizers,
    open fuse cut-outs, disconnecting switches,
    lightning arresters.

Poles--Creosoted wood, base pole 25-foot Class 6

Power Supply--National Power and Light Co. (ENALUF)

Delivery Points--
    Masaya - 100 KW
    Tipitapa - 150 KW

Supply Characteristics--
    7.6/13.2 KV Grounded Wye
    three-phase
    60 cycles
    5 percent regulation

System Capacity--Not to exceed 6 volts drop at av-
    erage of 100 KWH/month/consumer

Construction Standards--Standards as prescribed by
    REA.

Grade Construction--Light loading zone requirements
    of U.S. NESC.

Type System--Primary loop with radial taps.

Financial Aspects

The estimated cost of the entire project was
$483,300. The borrower was to contribute local
currency financing amounting to $83,300. The con-
tribution was in the form of services donated by
the National Energy Commission. These services
included preloan activities, training of personnel,
and the engineering and construction of lines.

In addition to the direct expenses to be covered by the AID loan and the borrower's contribution, grant funds for technical assistance were expended on the project.

Included in the loan were funds for construction of a headquarters building for the cooperative in Masaya. Also included in the loan were funds for reloaning by the cooperative to its members to finance housewiring and the purchase of electrical appliances.

Repayment of the loan by the cooperative was to be over a 25-year period with a 5-year grace period and an interest rate of 2 percent per annum. Table 110 describes project costs.

Organization

The Tisma Rural Electric Cooperative was formally organized on April 11, 1962. Its purpose was to acquire, distribute and supply electric power to its members for agricultural and industrial use.

Before beginning information meetings, Smith discussed the project with the director of Agricultural Extension. Extension personnel in the cooperative area then helped conduct some of the meetings. Almost all of the meetings were held out-of-doors.

At each meeting a complete explanation of the purpose of the meeting was given to those attending. Following the explanation a film on rural electrification in the United States was shown to the group. Smith reported the film most helpful to show conditions before electricity was available and after a rural electric cooperative was formed which brought electricity to the farm and home.

At the conclusion of each meeting the group discussed the next steps in forming the cooperative. Prepared questions and answers about the cooperative were read at the meeting and each person was

TABLE 110

Estimate of Costs for Tisma Rural Electric Cooperative, 1963
(in dollars)

Item	Miles of Line	Cost per Mile	Local Currency	Foreign Currency	Total Cost
Distribution Facilities					
A. Primary system					
Single-phase-2-wire	77.1	2,100	63,400	113,300	176,700
V-phase-3-wire	2.8	2,650	2,880	5,300	8,180
Three-phase-4 wire	33.7	3,000	39,520	70,800	100,320
B. Secondary system					
Secondary service	37.2	1,500	21,800	39,100	60,900
Total:					356,100
Headquarters Facilities					
A. Office building			11,600	--	11,600
B. Warehouse-Garage			2,700	--	2,700
Total:					14,300
All Others					
A. General plant equipment					
1. Construction & maintenance			--	14,600	14,600
2. Office			1,400	700	2,100
B. Contingency (10 % of plant)			10,700	25,000	35,700
					(Continued)

275

TABLE 110 (Continued)

Item	Miles of Line	Cost per Mile	Local Currency	Foreign Currency	Total Cost
C. Operating funds for first year			25,100	--	25,100
D. Special funds for financing housewiring, appliances, etc.			3,000	7,000	10,000
Total:					87,500
Preloan Expenses					
A. Orientation campaign			1,100	--	1,100
B. Preliminary map survey			2,900	--	2,900
C. Sign-up campaign			3,400	--	3,400
D. Complete field survey & final mapping			10,000	--	10,000
E. Engineering & feasibility study			2,900	--	2,900
F. Legal organization			2,300	--	2,300
G. Loan application preparation			1,400	--	1,400
H. Loan negotiation			1,400	--	1,400
Total:					25,400
Grand Total:					483,300

given a copy to take home. After all questions
from the group were answered, persons were asked to
volunteer to help sign up members. A meeting was
then held with the volunteers at the close of the
general session.

On Sunday, April 1, 1962, the members of the
cooperative met in a legal meeting in Masaya.
Wilfred Mast, the U.S. engineering consultant, was
present. Another legal meeting was held a week
later on April 8. Six members were elected to the
Board of Directors. The board then elected a president and secretary.

The constitution of the cooperative was prepared by the attorney for the National Energy Commission, Ricardo Sanchez. Another legal meeting
was held Wednesday, April 11. The constitution was
signed by 26 members and the cooperative became a
legal organization.

Construction

In accordance with the self-help aspect of the
project, it was planned that construction would be
completed by the "force account" method. Construction crews were to be trained by a U.S. rural electrification specialist and the National Energy Commission. It was thought that this procedure would
allow local labor to be trained for the specialized
jobs during the construction phases of the project
so that they would be available to the cooperative
for the operation and maintenance of the system.
The relatively small size of the project was not
conducive to receiving bids from contractors outside Nicaragua. If outside contractors had been
employed to build the system, the cooperative would
have been without trained technical help after completion of construction.

It was necessary to import conductors, transformers, meters, protective equipment and hardware
and poles. The cooperative also imported three
four-wheel drive vehicles and a pole trailer. This

equipment was to be used for maintenance after completion of construction.

Three months were necessary to obtain materials imported from the United States. Construction on the lines began in December, 1965.

Operation

The cooperative is privately owned. Its governing body consists of (1) the member's General Assembly, (2) the Board of Directors and (3) the Board of Control.

The General Assembly, composed of the entire membership, is the highest authority. Direction and administration of the cooperative is vested in a Board of Directors. The board consists of six members elected by the General Assembly, including a president and a secretary. Officers of the board serve for one year while all board members serve three-year terms.

The manager is appointed by the Board of Directors. He has direct management of the operations of the cooperative under supervision of the Board of Directors. The manager may not engage in any other business related to the affairs of the cooperative. Administrative personnel were obtained in Masaya, where the cooperative office is located.

The General Assembly also elects a Board of Control, composed of a president, a secretary and a General Assembly member. The functions of this board include verification of audits and supervision of the administrators. Bylaws of the cooperative set forth the manner in detail in which the cooperative is to be operated.

PRE-ELECTRIFICATION SURVEY

A survey of ten rural consumers and two schools in the Tisma area was conducted in April, 1965.

Intended Uses of Electricity

As would be expected, all ten consumers planned to use electricity for lights. The number of light bulbs per consumer varied from 1 to 26. The average was 10 bulbs per farm.

Anticipated use of radios and electric irons among the potential consumers was quite high--90 percent. But the greatest use of electricity was expected to be for pumping water. Among the ten consumers, there were ten water systems being planned. All but two consumers expected to pump water with electricity. Of the two remaining, one thought he might install a water system. He had a small generating plant and was using electricity for lights, fan, radio and television, but was still using a bucket and rope to get water from an open well. One consumer expected to have three water systems. The farm had six houses and the pumps would be used by all houses. In addition to the pressure water systems, two pumps solely for irrigation were being planned.

Refrigerators and television sets were also important. Four consumers already had refrigerators and three were planning to buy them. Two of the refrigerators on hand were gas, one was kerosene and one was electric. The owners planned to replace the gas and kerosene refrigerators within three years. Five consumers were planning to use television sets. Two sets had already been purchased. Forty percent of the sample planned to use electric fans. One member had two 2-horsepower milk coolers and wanted to replace them with a 5-horsepower motor.

Intended uses of electricity within three years after energization of the system were as shown in Table 111. The size, number and use of the electric motors were as shown in Table 112.

TABLE 111

Intended Uses of Electricity within Three
Years by Ten Farmers in Tisma, 1965

Appliance	Number
Incandescent bulb	78
Fluorescent tube	20
Radio	9
Iron	9
Refrigerator	7
Electric motor	17
Television	5
Fan	4
Heat lamp	4
Freezer	1
Blender	1
Tape recorder	1

Source: Consumer Survey.

TABLE 112

Size, Number and Use of Electric Motors within
Three Years by Ten Farmers in Tisma, 1965

Motor Size	Number	Use
1/4 HP	1	Shell corn
1 HP	6	Pump water
2 HP	4	Pump water
3 HP	2	Irrigate
4 HP	1	Irrigate
5 HP	2	Cool milk

Source: Consumer Survey.

Anticipated Benefits and Costs

Nine of the ten members thought electricity
would save time. Six thought it would reduce their
operating costs. Four said it would enable them to
irrigate and increase production. Two thought it
would increase their income and one said it would
mean less work on the farm. One member did not
know whether electricity would provide any benefits
for him. He was planning to use only one light
bulb and no other electrical appliances.

Of the sample, 40 percent expected to pay more
for electricity than they were presently paying for
fuels that electricity would replace. Thirty percent expected to pay less and 30 percent didn't
have any opinion as to whether it would cost more,
less or the same. Of the 40 percent that thought
it would cost more, 20 percent expected to pay this
increased cost by using their savings, 10 percent
expected to increase production and 10 percent expected to obtain additional work.

Previous Electrification

Six of the ten members were using electricity
produced by small generating plants. One member
had bought electricity previously from a neighbor
but it was no longer available. He had paid C $12
a month to use three light bulbs and one radio. It
was available about three hours each evening.

The six members who were using electricity
were paying from C $32 to C $220 a month and using
it from 3 to 13 hours a day. Ratio of monthly cost
per hour of daily use varied from C $8 to C $30.
This was the cost of fuel only and did not include
depreciation and maintenance of the generating
plant. Variation in cost can be attributed to size
of the plant, number of appliances used and care
and management of the equipment.

Two of the members used electricity 3 hours a
day; one used it 4 hours, one used it 5 hours, and

one used it 13 hours. The member using electricity
13 hours operated a dairy. He used electric lights
and milk coolers from 4 to 11 a.m. and from 4 to
10 p.m. Another member using electricity 5 hours a
day also operated a dairy. He used lights from 6
to 10 p.m. and from 1 to 2 a.m. Table 113 gives
the members, hours of consumption, cost per month
and uses.

It is interesting to note that the two consumers using the least number of appliances were
paying the most per hour for their electricity.

Land Use, Farm Size and Ownership

It was estimated that approximately half of
the farms in the Tisma area were operated by owners
while the other half were rented or handled by
other arrangements. In some cases an administrator
was placed on the farm to handle its management for
an agreed salary. In other cases, the owner lived
in town and visited the farm almost every day. He
managed the farm and hired workers to do the farming. Sizes of farms and uses of land among those
interviewed were as shown in Table 114.

TABLE 113

Use of Private Generating Plants by Ten
Farmers in Tisma, 1965

Farm No.	Hours of Use	Monthly Cost (C $)	Uses of Electricity
1	4	32.00	Lights, iron, water
2	13	220.00	Lights, milk cooler
5	3	70.00	Lights, radio, iron, fan
7	4	110.00	Lights, radio
8	3	60.00	Lights, radio, television
9	5	150.00	Lights

Source: Consumer Survey.

TABLE 114

Size of Farms in Manzanas and Use of Land
on Ten Farms in Tisma, 1965

Farm	Cotton	Tomatoes	Pasture	Corn	Other*	Total Area
1	120	-	-	-	-	120
2	110	-	200	40	550	900
3	-	1	-	2	25	28
4	-	-	-	11	10	21
5	15	-	-	-	-	15
6	6	-	15	9	-	30
7	-	-	260	40	-	300
8	10	5	5	-	-	20
9	100	-	482	60	8	650
10	-	-	3	11	21	35

*Bananas, platano, sesame, mountain land.

Source: Consumer Survey.

Seven of the members interviewed owned their
own land and three were administrators of the farms
employed by absentee owners for an agreed salary.
None of the members rented the land they farmed;
however, two of the owners rented out some of their
land to other farmers. One owner rented out 24
manzanas for pasture at C $100 per manzana per year.
Another owner rented out 100 manzanas for cotton
production at C $300 per manzana.

Seven of the ten farmers planned to buy more
land during the next three years. Two did not plan
to change the size of their farms and one planned
to sell one fourth of a manzana and wanted C $1,000
for this land. He owned 28 manzanas and was renting out 24.

Respondent Information

All of the members interviewed were married. They ranged in age from 23 to 71 and had from 2 to 11 dependents. Most had completed only a few years of school. Two did not have any formal schooling and two had completed eight years of school. Only three said they could read well, four said fair and three said poor. The age, marital status, number of dependents, years of school completed and ability to read for each member was as shown in Table 115.

Only three of the members belonged to a community organization. One was a member of Cooperativa Algondera de Nicaragua, a cotton cooperative. Another belonged to the Union de Agricultores, an association of small farmers. The third member was treasurer of a committee to build a church.

TABLE 115

Age, Number of Dependents, Years of School and
Ability to Read of Ten Farmers in Tisma, 1965

Consumer Number	Age	No. of Dependents	Years of School	Ability to Read
1	54	5	5	Fair
2	71	2	3	Fair
3	65	4	0	Poor
4	52	2	3	Fair
5	48	3	8	Good
6	40	5	0	Poor
7	37	4	3	Poor
8	53	2	3	Fair
9	38	3	6	Good
10	23	11	8	Good

Source: Consumer Survey.

Educational Facilities

Two schools were surveyed to determine if electricity would be used and, if so, for what purposes. One school was located in Zambrano and the other was in Tisma. The poor relationship between the parents of the students and the management of the Tisma school was discussed previously.

The Zambrano school, Escuela Ivan Mann Arcia, was an Alliance for Progress project. A sign on the school grounds explains that the school was built as a cooperative project by the Government of Nicaragua and the United States. The school had one teacher who lived in Managua. She could have lived at the school if facilities had been adequate (space was provided for living facilities in construction of the school). The teacher spent two hours a day commuting from Managua which was 29 kilometers from the school. She rode a bus most of the distance but also had to walk approximately 3 kilometers. The 44 year-old teacher was married and had six dependents. She had completed nine years of school.

Use of electricity at the school was expected to be for lights (five bulbs), radio, iron and fan. The school had an open well. A rope and bucket was used to obtain water. One of the school's two classrooms was vacant and could have been used for teaching. The teacher said they could have evening classes for adults when electricity became available.

The Tisma school, Escuela Benjamin Zeledon, was expected to use 25 fluorescent lights, one fan, one refrigerator and one motor for pumping water. The school did not have electricity and the 204 students had to bring their own water bottles to school. Electricity also was expected to improve conditions for the director living at the school. In addition, the director planned to have classes from 6 to 8 p.m. five nights a week for adults. Classes would teach reading, writing and arithmetic.

The director was 25 years old, had completed
13 years of school and had a teachers license. He
was single and had no dependents, but did help his
parents and brothers.

BENCH MARK DATA

Production inputs were subtracted from farm
products marketed to determine income for each of
the ten farms surveyed. Production and costs for
1964 were used as the base period data.

Questions also were asked during the survey
to determine each farmer's knowledge of cooperative
organization procedures and operations. Finally,
to establish bench mark information, farmers were
asked questions concerning their values and attitudes.

Base Period Input

Labor, equipment and energy, which could be
replaced with electricity, and variable inputs such
as seed, feed, fertilizer and insecticides were determined in the interviews (see Table 116). Fuels
used for lighting and the annual and monthly costs
for each farm consumer were as shown in Table 117.
Value of fertilizer, insecticide, seed, pasture
rental and concentrate for each consumer was as
shown in Table 118.

Much heavier concentrations of fertilizer and
insecticide were used on cotton than on other crops.
Approximately 3 quintales of fertilizer were used
for 1 manzana of cotton while 1 quintal of fertilizer was used for 1 manzana of corn. Roughly 2
quintales of insecticide were applied to 1 manzana
of cotton, while 1 quintal of insecticide was used
for every 2 manzanas of corn or sesame.

Base Period Output

Cotton, milk and corn were the most important
market crops. A comparison of yields and the market

TABLE 116

Value of Base Period Inputs for Ten Farms
in Tisma, 1964
(in cordobas)

Farm	Labor	Energy	Variable Inputs	Total Inputs
1	168,000	1,128	54,285	223,413
2	120,180	4,060	53,860	178,100
3	--	36	--	36
4	6,968	42	--	7,010
5	2,400	1,300	4,068	7,768
6	3,120	210	2,000	5,330
7	9,360	1,318	13,832	24,510
8	19,900	900	4,796	25,596
9	52,335	1,794	20,160	74,289
10	11,490	144	8,420	20,054
Total:	393,753	10,932	161,421	566,106

Source: Consumer Survey.

TABLE 117

Value of Fuels for Lighting on Ten Farms
in Tisma, 1964

Farm	Fuels	Annual Cost	Monthly Cost
		(in cordobas)	
1	Diesel, oil*	386	32.17
2	Diesel, oil	2,640	220.00
3	Kerosene	109	9.08
4	Kerosene	84	7.00
5	Gasoline, oil*	1,300	108.33
6	Kerosene, candle	210	17.50
7	Gasoline, oil*	110	9.17
8	Gasoline, oil*	900	75.00
9	Gasoline, oil*	1,794	149.50
10	Kerosene	144	12.00
	Average	768	63.98

*Consumer has a small generator that is being used for appliances in addition to lighting.

Source: Consumer Survey.

TABLE 118

Value of Variable Inputs for Ten Farms
in Tisma, 1964
(in cordobas)

Farm	Fertil- izer	Insec- ticides	Seeds	Other	Total
1	10,500	42,000	1,785	--	54,285
2	14,000	37,000	2,860	--	54,860
3	--	--	--	--	--
4	--	--	--	--	--
5	1,050	3,000	18	--	4,068
6	--	--	--	2,000[a]	2,000
7	--	--	--	13,832[b]	13,832
8	1,160	3,600	36	--	4,796
9	3,000	--	--	17,160[b]	20,160
10	--	500	--	7,920[b]	8,420
Total:	29,710	86,100	4,699	40,912	161,421

[a]Renting pasture for dairy cows.

[b]Concentrate for dairy cows.

Source: Consumer Survey.

prices received by each of the consumers shows considerable variation (see Tables 119, 120 and 121).
Total agricultural output during 1964 for the ten
consumers is shown in Table 122.

Four of the ten farmers interviewed relied on
one product for their income. Three of the ten received 100 percent of their income from cotton.
One received all of his income from milk. Thirty
percent of the sample depended upon two products,
20 percent on three products and 10 percent on four
products. Percentage of income from various
sources for each consumer was as shown in Table 123.

TABLE 119

Cotton Production, Price, Area, Yield and
Fertilizer Application on Four Farms
in Tisma, 1964

Farm	Market Price (C $)	No. of Manzanas	Production in Quintales	Yield per Manzana	Quintales of Fertilizer per M.
1	60.00	120	4,500	37.5	2.1
2	60.00	110	5,000	45.5	3.2
5	60.00	15	450	30.0	2.0
8	58.00	10	420	42.0	2.9

Source: Consumer Survey.

TABLE 120

Milk Production, Price, Number of Cows and Annual
Production per Cow on Five Farms in Tisma, 1964

Farm	Market Price (C $)	No. of Cows	Production in Gals.	Production per Cow
2	3.50	85	36,400	428
6	3.20	20	5,475	274
7	4.20	45	14,600	324
9	3.00	70	27,375	391
10	4.40	24	4,380	183

Source: Consumer Survey.

TABLE 121

Corn Production, Price, Area and Yield on
Ten Farms in Tisma, 1964

Farm	Market Price (C $)	No. of Manzanas	Production in Quintales	Yield per Manzana
3	30.00	2	10	5.0
4	30.00	11	150	13.6
9	30.00	60	990	16.5
10	30.00	11	66	6.0

Source: Consumer Survey.

TABLE 122

Value of Base Period Output on Ten Farms in Tisma, 1964 (in cordobas)

Farm	Cotton	Milk	Corn	Other	Total Value
1	252,000	--	--	--	252,000
2	300,000	127,400	--	--	427,400
3	--	--	150	2,674	2,824
4	--	--	4,500	9,000	13,500
5	27,000	--	--	--	27,000
6	--	17,520	--	--	17,520
7	61,320	--	--	--	61,320
8	24,360	--	--	10,000	34,360
9	--	82,125	18,000	30,000	130,125
10	--	19,272	1,615	3,600	24,487
Total:	664,680	246,317	24,265	55,274	990,536

Source: Consumer Survey.

TABLE 123

Percentage of Income from Various Products on Ten Farms in Tisma, 1964

Farm	Cotton	Milk	Corn	Other	Nonagricultural
1	100	--	--	--	--
2	70	30	--	--	--
3	--	--	5	95	--
4	--	--	33	67	--
5	100	--	--	--	--
6	--	100	--	--	--
7	100	--	--	--	--
8	71	--	--	29	--
9	--	63	14	23	--
10	--	79	6	15	--

Source: Consumer Survey.

Base Period Income

Base farm income varied greatly. A small farm operated by an elderly man had an annual income of C $2,788. A much larger farm operated by an administrator and having six houses for workers had an income in 1964 of C $249,300. Average base income for the ten farms was C $42,443. At an exchange rate of C $7.00 per $1.00, average annual farm income was $6,063. Table 124 shows base income for all farms in the sample.

Cooperative Knowledge

In an effort to establish bench marks in awareness of some operations of an electric cooperative, each consumer surveyed was asked a series of questions.

TABLE 124

Value of Base Period Income for Ten Farms
in Tisma, 1964
(in cordobas)

Farm	Base Output	Base Input	Base Income
1	252,000	223,413	28,587
2	427,400	178,100	249,300
3	2,824	36	2,788
4	13,500	7,101	6,490
5	27,000	7,768	19,232
6	17,520	5,330	12,190
7	61,320	24,510	36,810
8	34,360	25,596	8,764
9	130,125	74,289	55,836
10	24,487	20,054	4,433
Total:	990,536	566,106	424,430

Source: Consumer Survey.

When asked how they would describe an electric
cooperative, 20 percent of the sample said they
could not describe it. Thirty percent described it
as a cooperative organization or group of people to
bring lights to the houses. Twenty percent simply
said it was an organization of people for the purpose of obtaining services at a lower price. And
10 percent said it was an association of members
that make use of the services of a cooperative and
then pay for the services. Roughly 50 percent had
an idea of how to describe an electric cooperative.

Only one member thought the cooperative was
owned by the government. Four said it was not
owned by the government and half the members interviewed said they did not know. Thus, only 40 percent were aware of cooperative ownership. Ninety
percent thought the manager was elected by the members. The other 10 percent didn't know. Thus,
none of the members interviewed were aware that the
manager is selected by the Board of Directors. All
of the sample knew that anyone in the area could
become a member of the cooperative. Only 30 percent
thought correctly that the electric cooperative
would not pay dividends to the members every year.
Sixty percent thought it would, and 10 percent
didn't know. Almost all, 90 percent, knew that
each member of the electric cooperative had one
vote.

On awareness of what an electric cooperative
is and how it functions, the sample scored 26 out
of a possible 60. Therefore, it appears that the
members were only 43 percent aware of factors concerning description and operation of an electric
cooperative.

Values and Attitudes

Each respondent was told to assume that he had
a son, and to tell what he would like him to grow
up to be. Opinion was well divided among doctors,
lawyers and engineers: 30 percent said a doctor,
30 percent said a lawyer, and 30 percent said an

engineer. The other 10 percent said whatever profession the child chooses. Only one of the ten
members interviewed indicated that he wanted his
child to have anything to do with agriculture. He
said he would like his son to be an agricultural
engineer.

When asked where the money was coming from to
build the rural electric distribution system, 70
percent said the United States. The other 30 percent said they didn't know.

Members were asked to tell their goal or ambi-
tion in life. Forty percent simply said to work
(trabajar). This can be interpreted broadly to
mean that they wanted to continue having good
health and an opportunity to continue working. Another 40 percent said they wanted to improve their
level of living. The two remaining were divided
between making money and becoming an experienced
farmer.

To determine the attitudes of members toward
the administration of their country and local community, they were told to take into consideration
development during the past three years. They were
then asked if they thought the national government
had done a good job. If they said "No," they were
to explain. Fifty percent of the members thought
the national government had done a good job. Twenty percent said no and 30 percent said they didn't
know. The two members replying no explained that
the national government had not done anything to
help the Tisma community, especially in building
highways or improving streets. It appeared that
those saying they didn't know actually thought no
but felt it was better to be noncommittal. If this
were so, it would divide opinion equally about the
national government.

A slightly larger percentage had definite
opinions about the work of the municipal government.
Twenty percent said the Municipio had done a good
job and 60 percent said it had not. Twenty percent

said they didn't know. Those saying no explained
that the Municipio had not done anything. One member said he had not seen any progress in the 11
years that he had lived in Tisma. The 20 percent
who thought the Municipio had done a good job explained that it had recently built a large ditch
around Tisma to divert water during the rainy season.

Even a larger percentage--70 percent--thought
the local school was not being run properly. Twenty percent thought it was, and 10 percent said they
did not know. But none of the members replying yes
or saying they did not know had children attending
the school. The 70 percent saying no did have
children attending the Tisma school. They did not
think that the staff had the ability to direct the
school and said it was disorganized.

Seventy percent of those interviewed said
their neighbors had been cooperative and helpful.
Thirty percent said they had not. They simply explained that their neighbors did not want to coop-
erate with them.

Eighty percent thought living conditions in
the area had improved. Twenty percent said they
had remained the same. Of the 80 percent, half
said there were more job opportunities. The other
half said they had more material things such as a
radio, a television, better transportation, more
community facilities such as a new school and people were more enthusiastic about working.

PROJECTION OF EFFECT ON INCOME

The effect of electrification on income for
the ten farms surveyed was projected for three
years. Farmers were asked what changes they intended to make in their production plans within
three years after electricity became available.
Assuming these changes would be carried out, farm

inputs and outputs were calculated for that period and projected income was obtained.

Estimated farm income three years after the availability of electricity was compared with base farm income to determine the effect of rural electrification on income.

Production Plans

Seventy percent of those interviewed expected to change their production plans after electricity became available. Of the seven who intended to change production plans, one said he would irrigate 80 manzanas of vegetables, pasture and bananas. He also wanted to milk 140 cows instead of 85 as at present. Two members said they would raise chickens; one expected to raise 1,800 chickens a year. Another was planning an ice plant and gas station. Another planned to irrigate pasture and increase milk production from 40 gallons a day to 80 gallons. Another was planning to irrigate 5 manzanas of platano. The sixth member was milking 70 cows and he planned to milk 100 within three years after electricity became available.

Milk production varied among the sample from about .5 gallon per cow per day to 1.5 gallons. This included all cows in the dairy herd.

Projected Input

Projecting factors of production on the basis of anticipated changes in production plans and projecting electrical costs for base fuel costs gave the results shown in Table 125.

With electricity the value of inputs would be 18 percent higher on the sample of ten farms. Energy costs were projected to be higher on six farms and lower on the remaining four with the availability of electricity. Input costs for labor energy and variable factors were projected to increase for the sample.

TABLE 125

Projected Value of Inputs Three Years after
the Availability of Electricity on
Ten Farms in Tisma
(in cordobas)

Farm	Labor	Energy	Variable Inputs	Total Inputs
1	169,088	796	56,385	226,269
2	151,500	1,744	53,860	207,104
3	--	120	--	120
4	10,296	796	9,100	20,192
5	2,400	1,020	4,068	7,488
6	3,120	423	2,000	5,543
7	18,720	828	27,664	47,212
8	22,600	825	4,796	28,248
9	71,352	1,356	34,320	107,028
10	11,490	928	8,420	20,838
Total:	460,566	8,863	200,613	670,042

Source: Consumer Survey.

Projected Output

Based on changes in production plans with the
availability of electricity, projected output would
be as shown in Table 126.

According to production plans, value of production of cotton, milk and meat would increase.
Value of total farm marketings three years after
the availability of electricity were projected to
increase 17 percent for the ten farms as a group.

Projected Income

Projected input was subtracted from projected
output for each of the ten farms. The gap between
the low-income farm and the high-income farm became
even wider. On the small farm the elderly owner
intended to use electricity for consumptive purposes

TABLE 126

Projected Value of Outputs Three Years after
the Availability of Electricity on
Ten Farms in Tisma
(in cordobas)

Farm	Cotton	Milk	Corn	Other	Total
1	252,000	--	--	4,200	256,200
2	300,000	164,780	--	--	464,780
3	--	--	150	2,674	2,824
4	--	--	4,500	30,600	35,100
5	27,000	--	--	--	27,000
6	--	17,520	--	--	17,520
7	122,640	--	--	--	122,640
8	24,360	--	--	19,000	43,360
9	--	117,300	18,000	30,000	165,300
10	--	19,272	1,615	3,600	24,487
Total:	726,000	318,872	24,265	90,074	1,159,211

Source: Consumer Survey.

only, thus increasing expenditures for energy.
With the same output his farm income decreased.

On the high-income farm plans were being made
to increase production. Electricity also would
cost less than the fuels it would replace; therefore, income on the farm would increase. Table 127
shows projected income three years after the availability of electricity on each of the ten farms in
the Tisma area.

Effect on Income

When projected income was compared with base
income for each of the ten farms, it showed that
income with the availability of electricity would
increase on seven farms and decrease on three. On
the three farms where income would decrease no
plans had been made to use electricity in the farming operations. Output would remain the same while

TABLE 127

Projected Income Three Years after the
Availability of Electricity on
Ten Farms in Tisma
(in cordobas)

Farm	Projected Output	Projected Input	Projected Income
1	256,200	226,269	29,931
2	464,780	207,104	257,676
3	2,824	120	2,704
4	35,100	20,192	14,908
5	27,000	7,488	19,512
6	17,520	5,543	11,977
7	122,640	47,212	75,428
8	43,360	28,248	15,112
9	165,300	107,028	58,272
10	24,487	20,838	3,649
Total:	1,159,211	670,042	489,169

energy costs would increase with the intended uses
of electricity for consumptive purposes.

Electricity generally had a greater effect on
income for those farms producing milk. Table 128
shows the effect of electricity on income for each
of the ten farms. Income for the ten farms as a
group would increase 15.3 percent within three
years after electricity becomes available if production plans are carried out.

INITIAL IMPACT

In May, 1970, the manager of the Rural Electric Cooperative reported that television sets,
blenders, irons, refrigerators and other electrical
appliances were being used in many homes in the
Tisma area. Electric motors were being used in the

TABLE 128

Projected Effect on Income of the
Availability of Electricity on
Ten Farms in Tisma
(in cordobas)

Farm	Base Income	Projected Income	Effect on Income
1	28,587	29,931	1,344
2	249,300	257,676	8,376
3	2,788	2,704	(-84)
4	6,490	14,908	8,418
5	19,232	19,512	280
6	12,190	11,977	(-213)
7	36,810	75,428	38,618
8	8,764	15,112	6,348
9	55,836	58,272	2,436
10	4,433	3,649	(-784)
Total:	424,430	489,169	64,739

Source: Consumer Survey.

rural areas to pump water for livestock and for irrigation of field crops. Milk coolers, grain shell-
ers and other farm equipment were being operated
electrically. The manager reported that, in his
opinion, electrical energy had definitely raised
the living standard of the residents in the Tisma
area.

It was reported that schools were providing
adult education courses at night and that programs
for providing potable water and developing sewage
systems were being planned in the villages.

By 1970 the cooperative listed 950 members and
claimed to serve about 8,000 people. It was estimated that about 200 homes and five farms in the
cooperative area were still without electricity.
Among the electric cooperative's membership were
909 village homes, 15 farms, 13 small industries,

2 large industries, 3 cottage industries, 6 schools,
5 churches and 2 community centers. The cooperative employed 17 people and claimed to have helped
create employment in the area, principally through
the provision of central station electricity to two
large cotton gins, a feed mill and a small textile
plant.

6

FINDINGS:
IMPLICATIONS
FOR
DEVELOPMENT

One yardstick for measuring the economic and
technical development of a country is its use of
power. In many of the less developed countries the
main sources of power still are human beings and
domestic animals. As the countries have developed
economically and socially, mechanical energy has
replaced human and animal labor. In the more developed countries, electric power consumption has
trended upward with growth of the national economy.

As the national economies have grown, rural
electrification also has grown. Electricity in
agriculture has the advantage over other types of
energy of providing not only power but also lighting, radio, television and many other conveniences.
It has the disadvantage in agriculture of being dependent on a relatively expensive distribution network.

The high cost of the distribution system is
not the only factor limiting rural electrification
in the less developed countries. Lack of understanding of the benefits and uses of electricity in
agriculture is perhaps even more important. Low
densities of population also have been important in
some areas.

In some less developed countries the problem
is even more basic. There is a lack of or an under-
development of natural sources of energy such as
coal, oil or water power. Also, the stage of development of the economy may be such that it is not
profitable to substitute mechanical energy for human
and animal labor.

A basis for rural electrification is not only
a reliable source of power but also a sufficient demand for productive purposes. Subsistence farming
does not provide this basis. Therefore, rural electrification makes a greater contribution to growth
of the national economy in areas where commercial
agriculture is practiced.

Generally, insufficient availability of capital for construction of rural distribution lines
and the assumption by those in power that rural income is insufficient to permit the farm population
to purchase electric energy have been the major deterrents to rural electrification in developing
countries.

For rural electrification to be a justifiable
part of an overall development program, it must ex-
ert a favorable effect on prerequisites to develop-
ment--minimum levels of effective government, education and motivation--and factors affecting the
rate of development--human and natural resources,
capital accumulation, technical knowledge and institutional structure.

With information obtained from surveys of the
pilot rural electric cooperative areas and from results of previous studies of rural electrification
in more developed countries, an examination is made
of the implications of cooperative rural electrification for development.

GOVERNMENT

Operation of the pilot rural electric cooperatives will continue to be in close association with

state and national governments. Personnel of the
government organizations will have an opportunity
to work closely with the rural people. This close
working relationship will permit government administrators to become better acquainted with the problems of rural development.

Improved knowledge of the existing rural situation and an understanding of agricultural problems
will assist the government officials in doing a
better job of public administration. As the organ
of public administration becomes more competent,
technical knowledge and capital investment will pay
greater dividends.

Politics has been a definite factor in organization of the Sevilla-Caicedonia cooperative in
Colombia. Extremists were almost successful in preventing the electric cooperative from being formed
in Sevilla. If the opposition had been successful
in blocking the cooperative, the town of Sevilla
would have continued to have an antiquated electric
distribution system and the remainder of the Municipio would have been without electric service.

Members of the Municipal Council leading the
opposition to the cooperative also had personal interests at stake. The most vociferous leaders were
those using a substantial amount of unmetered electricity for a minimal amount of money. The cooperative has installed meters and is charging consumers
according to the amount of electricity used. Thus,
the cooperative has instituted reforms in Sevilla
that will facilitate development.

EDUCATION

Implications of the survey of rural schools
were that cooperative rural electrification would
have a favorable effect on educational development.
Electric lighting has made it possible for study
room conditions to be improved substantially. Electricity also is making it possible for schools to
conduct adult education classes in the evenings.

Rural electrification has improved living conditions for the teachers residing at the schools. Schools have purchased electric lighting, radios, irons, fans, refrigerators, water pumps and in some cases television sets and electric stoves. Electric water pumps have made it possible for some schools to have water for the first time. For other schools water pumps are providing a means of obtaining potable water.

Cooperative organization of electric energy distribution can help bring teachers and parents together and facilitate understanding of school and community problems. This need was apparent in about half of the schools surveyed.

Radio and television reception made possible by rural electrification can play a significant role in education of the rural people. Electrification of the individual home also will extend the time an individual can read and study.

Operation of the cooperative organization is contributing to the general education and training of the rural population. Members are becoming better informed of community activities and needs through the rural electric cooperative meetings. They also have an opportunity for training in leadership through cooperative meetings and activities.

The cooperative mechanism provides training for rural people. Each member of the rural electric cooperative receives business training in the process of paying monthly bills. For many of the people, this is their first experience in receiving periodic bills. They are learning that they must make payment on schedule or their electric service will be discontinued. This business practice is consistent with the aim of a cooperative which is "to perform the business activities, selling or buying of its member firms (households) in the way which is most profitable for them."[1]

General implications of cooperative rural electrification for education and training are

implicit in the cooperative organization. The cooperative movement has always regarded education as
one of its basic aims. Promotion of education was
among the original Rochdale principles.* Almost
all types of cooperatives make regular financial
allocations for educational purposes.

Training of cooperative staffs has become increasingly important. Every aspect of administration and management has become more important as
the organizations have become more complex. Leadership in the cooperative organization has tended
to pass from committees to full-time professional
employees. Staff training, therefore, has become
imperative to operation of an efficient well-run
business organization.

In many countries with highly developed cooperative movements, national associations have assumed leadership in providing training for employees of the cooperatives. In the cooperative rural
electrification movement in the United States, the
national association provides 46 different work-
shops, institutes and seminars annually for approximately 13,000 managers, directors, staff employees
and members of about 1,000 rural electric cooperatives.

Cooperative rural electrification also makes
possible the realization of educational television.
In some developing countries, programming for educational television is now underway with the cooperation of the U.S. Peace Corps.

Rural electrification has played an important
role in improving the economic and social level of
the people of Puerto Rico. It is planned that educational television will reach almost every school
in Puerto Rico. Large urban elementary and high
school buildings as well as rural one-room school

_____

*Rochdale, near Manchester, England, was one
of the earliest (1844) cooperative societies.

buildings will be included in the government-operated educational television network.[2]

What is happening in Puerto Rico's program to improve the quality of education could take place in any of the developing countries. But it will not be possible without rural electrification. And rural electrification through cooperatives increases the opportunity for improving education and training of the rural population.

MOTIVATION

Members of the electric cooperatives have become motivated to participate in community development. As an example, pilot rural electric cooperatives in Colombia, Nicaragua and Ecuador were able to obtain right-of-way easements without cost to build the distribution lines. Members of the cooperatives were willing to give these easements because they realized they were the owners of the electric distribution system.

In some cases owners donated land for construction of the cooperative office. In Ecuador land was donated for the site of a power generation station. In Nicaragua technical personnel marked trees that were to be cut down in order to make way for the distribution lines. Owners of the land where the trees were located then cut down the trees at their own expense.

Economic development planning must not overlook these human resources. It must take into consideration qualities of the community and the desire of the people to develop. "Growth depends on growers, upon human beings, on their outlook, on their will to achieve some objective, their capacity to achieve it measured, not only in terms of their skills, but in their health and strength and indeed in their spirit."[3]

The spirit of cooperation can be a valuable contribution to development. Cooperation between rural electric cooperatives in the United States

and new cooperatives in Latin America have contributed to their initial operating success. Meters, transformers, insulators and wire were donated by the rural electric cooperatives in Kentucky to help develop two cooperatives in Ecuador.
Similar programs have been developed between other
states and other developing countries.

"The links with community groups at various
levels, the reflection of appropriate interests
during the writing of the plan and during its implementation give people a sense of identification
with a process. The political and social factors
weave in and out and give strength to the fabric."[4]

HUMAN AND NATURAL RESOURCES

Basic elements of agriculture include climate,
labor and land management. Rural electrification
cannot influence climate except in a limited sense
through electrical control in a protected area such
as a greenhouse. In countries with areas of insufficient rainfall, it can influence productivity of
the land through irrigation. But in most cases rural electrification has its greatest influence on
manual labor. Management involves decisions on the
best methods of using labor and the degree to which
mechanization, including electrification, should be
introduced.

Mining can be important in rural areas and is
often made possible through rural electrification.
In the small village of Vijes, near Cali, Colombia,
electric power made it possible to start a marble
factory. Insufficient power had previously made
it impractical to extract the stone in nearby
hills. When the power authority brought central
station power to the rural area in 1962, the small
factory began operation. At the time of the survey in March, 1965, the factory employed 27 workers
and planned to double its operation.

While rural electrification can have a substantial effect on the development of natural resources, it has a greater influence on human

resources. Labor inputs constitute a major item of
cost in practically all types of rural activity.
The manner in which a rural enterprise utilizes its
labor resources--operator, family and hired labor--
has a great deal to do with both the money income
that can be obtained from its resources and the
amount of leisure time that the farm operator and
his family will have.[5]

Agricultural work in less developed countries
is characterized by a large amount of manual labor.
The availability of inexpensive labor, the limited
use for specialized equipment, the high cost of
machinery and the seasonality of production have
been deterrents to expanded use of farm equipment.
As the countries develop economically, however, the
cost of hired labor increases, problems develop in
obtaining and utilizing hired labor and a higher
opportunity cost for the operator's own labor make
it profitable to use more equipment than previously.

Experience in developed countries indicates
that labor wage rates increase much more rapidly
than prices of either electricity or equipment.
For example, an Iowa study compared the changes in
wages of hired labor with changes in the price of
electric energy and a few key types of labor-saving
equipment from 1940 to 1950.[6]

During this period the price of labor more
than tripled. This compared with an increase of
about 20 percent for the first 200 kilowatt-hours
of electricity used each month and a decrease in
the average cost per kilowatt-hour of all electricity used. Similarly, the price of electric motors
doubled during the same period, the price of electric water heaters increased 54 percent and that of
pressure water systems 36 percent. The change in
relative prices indicated that it would be profitable for farm operators to go further in substituting electrical equipment and electric energy for
labor than in the beginning of the period.

Therefore, a chief contribution of electrical
equipment to agricultural production is its use as

a substitute for labor. Substitution of electric
energy for labor may result directly in a lower
cost of production, but its importance is magnified
by the variable nature of labor requirements in agriculture.

Labor to supplement that of the operator and
his family in the Sevilla-Caicedonia area is needed
only during two peak periods of the year. This
labor requirement is typical not only of coffee-
growing areas but, of many other areas where different types of agriculture are practiced. If labor
requirements can be reduced during those critical
periods by substituting electrical equipment for
labor, the necessity of hiring labor may be reduced
or eliminated.

In some cases the work load on the farm requires an additional worker for only part of the
working day. Yet it is necessary to hire the worker for the entire day. Sometimes workers with the
necessary skill and experience cannot be obtained
to do certain jobs. In some types of farming, a
minimum of turnover in personnel is essential if
hired labor is to be satisfactory, because of the
time required to fit a new worker into the routine.
This was more true on the beef and dairy farms than
it was on the coffee farms. Although hired labor
on coffee farms has a rapid turnover, little training is required because the workers migrate to
other areas and do the same type of work the year
round.

When hired workers receive part of their wages
in board and room, an additional inconvenience is
imposed on the family. Some farm operators object
to taking hired workers into the family group not
only because of their influence on the children but
also because they make extra work. In some situations, electricity and electrical equipment would
offer a dependable substitute for hired labor.

Labor-saving equipment may also save scarce
family and operator time for use in other jobs on
the farm. Respondents in Sevilla and Caicedonia

indicated that this would be one of their principal
benefits from electricity. The time saved in tending fuel operated chick brooders may make it possible for the operator to raise more chickens or
devote more time to another enterprise.

Particularly in less developed countries, time
saved of the operator can be spent profitably in
giving more attention to farm management and the
business aspects of farming. Keeping abreast of
new developments in agricultural methods and price
changes will be increasingly important as the rural
economy of the country develops.

Not one of the farms surveyed indicated that
it would reduce the amount of hired labor after
electricity became available. The principal anticipated benefits were to save time for the operator,
provide security, reduce costs, increase production
and provide a more dependable source of power.
Findings of the survey were consistent with the
Iowa study that found that "most farmers said that
the principal effect of the introduction of labor-
saving equipment was to reduce the working hours of
the operator and his family or to increase the vol-
umè of production rather than to reduce hired labor." Nineteen percent of the Iowa farmers thought
"electricity had reduced the amount of family labor
used in production and 39 percent of the operators
thought their own working hours to be less than one
man-hour a day. However, about 13 percent attributed a saving of more than an hour a day to the effects of electricity and electrical equipment."[7]

This savings in labor of the operator as reported in the Iowa study is slightly less than that
recorded in a similar study in Great Britain.[8] In
a study of five farms in South West England it was
found that electricity made it possible for each
farm to save an average of 410 man-hours annually.
Another study of four farms by the University of
Bristol showed an average saving of work requirement of about 500 hours per farm per year, or a
fifth of a man's time on each.[9]

No attempt was made in the present study to determine the anticipated number of hours the farm operator might save with electricity. The Iowa and Great Britain studies indicate that the anticipated saving in time of farm operators in the pilot project areas could be realized and that their anticipated changes in production could be carried out with saved labor.

Another effect of rural electrification on human resource development is that it permits the use of family, elderly or partially incapacitated workers.[10] By eliminating heavy lifting, complicated routines and disagreeable tasks with the use of electricity and electrical equipment, it is frequently possible to utilize family labor or elderly or incapacitated workers for jobs that would otherwise require an able-bodied man. On coffee farms in Sevilla and Caicedonia work such as coffee dispulping could be carried out with electricity and family labor. The Iowa study showed that the wives of farm operators were separating cream and even milking cows, freeing the operator to carry out other work. Such could be the case in the pilot rural electric cooperative areas of Colombia, Costa Rica, Nicaragua and Ecuador.

Electrical equipment that reduces hard work makes it possible for a man to work longer hours with less fatigue. Reducing the amount of walking and eliminating the number of different operations needed to complete farm jobs is also a benefit. This is particularly important for work that is performed daily. One operator in Sevilla said he spent an hour a day filling and inspecting the oil heater for his baby chicks. This time would be eliminated almost entirely with an electric heater. In addition it would eliminate the danger of explosion of the fuel heater.

Labor requirements in most developing countries are highly seasonal as they were reported for the Iowa farmers. This means that the value of the farmer's time in terms of the alternative uses for

labor varies from season to season. Labor saved
during one season through the use of electricity
may have a high value, but during the slack season
the labor saved has little value.

Distribution of labor requirements on farms
can be improved by reducing labor requirements that
must be done during peak seasons. In the Iowa study
installation of a pressure water system was credit-
ed by 9 percent of the operators in the area with
saving 20 to 30 minutes of hand labor daily in wa-
tering livestock. Because of the antiquated methods
of obtaining water in less developed countries, the
saving of hand labor could be substantially higher.
Even though the saving in labor during a particular
season might have little economic value, its importance during another season could be great enough
to make the change profitable.

Another way to distribute labor requirements
more evenly is to shift jobs from a peak period to
periods in which demands for labor are lower. An
example of this in the United States was the shift
in time of the farrowing of baby pigs. It not only
distributed the labor more evenly but permitted
swine producers to take advantage of more favorable
pork prices. Labor in the pilot project areas
could be distributed more evenly throughout the
year through the diversification of production.

As reported previously, 36 percent of the farm
operators in Sevilla and Caicedonia said they would
diversify agricultural production increasing the
number of products per farm 33 percent. This undoubtedly will have a beneficial effect upon the
distribution of farm labor.

There are also implications that rural electrification will have a beneficial effect upon the
rate of population growth. The rapid increase in
population is the one variable that most limits the
rate of economic growth in the less developed countries. While there are no studies that have been
conducted on the effect of rural electrification on

population growth, there are some observations that
have been recorded.

India is placing great emphasis on a program
of rural electrification. The purpose is partly to
increase the acreage of irrigated land, partly to
provide power for small industries in the villages
and partly to increase radio communication between
remote villages and the cities. The Food Minister
said there was also another reason for electrification of the rural villages. In Madras, his home
state, 80 percent of the villages have electricity
and the birth rate in that state is about half as
large as the national birth rate. "In the dark
villages," the Food Minister has said, "the only
recreation at night is procreation and this is one
of our major problems."[11]

It is also interesting to note that there was
a declining birth rate for the rural areas of Puerto Rico during the 1950-60 decade. This was precisely the time period during which the Puerto Rico
Water Resources Authority launched its rural electrification program.

No research has been done, however, to show
there is a causal relationship. Certainly, the
heavy migration of the decade could have been an
influential factor. It is pointed out by a government agency of Puerto Rico that rural electrification opened a means of communication through which
birth control information was given to the public.
This may have had an effect on the birth rate of
the rural areas.[12]

TECHNICAL PROGRESS

Inefficient production techniques is a major
factor accounting for the low productivity of agriculture in developing countries. Low productivity
of agriculture in turn accounts to a great extent
for the poverty that is found in the rural areas of
the less developed countries. The fact that

developing countries are generally oriented toward
agriculture in itself is not a cuase of poverty
(although it is a factor affecting the economic
level of the country); the cause of poverty is the
low productivity in agriculture.[13]

There is no wonder-formula for curing the
problems of low productivity. Specific measures
can be formulated only after the particular causes
of low productivity have been determined. And the
formula to a great extent will depend upon the
country being considered.

One of the problems with increasing agricultural production in the developing countries is the
lack of adequate testing. Improved practices obtained by research may work fine in the experimental plots, but may be ineffective in other areas.
These failures result because conditions prevailing
in the experimental plot are not the same as in
other regions of the country. Soil and climatic
conditions may vary greatly within a country. No
recommendation of an improved practice should be
made until it has been thoroughly tested on farms
in the principal environmental areas of the country
concerned.[14]

In order to increase agricultural productivity
it is necessary for farmers to believe in the de-
sirability of change. They must also see an opportunity for personal gain from improved practices.
This is the area where rural electrification can
make its greatest contribution.

Prospects of rural electrification stimulated
80 farm operators in the project areas to the extent that they anticipated increasing production
14 percent. This appears to be a conservative estimate. In Switzerland, electrification of small
mountain farms resulted in an increase of some 25
percent in the annual production of hay and other
fodder crops. This increase was due mainly to the
effective distribution of liquid manure pumped by
electric motors, to otherwise inaccessible land.

On a 26-acre Austrian farm, production of the main
crops--rye, wheat, barley, potatoes, beets and hay
--was almost doubled after the farm had been electrified.[15]

Twenty-four percent of the respondents in Sevilla and Caicedonia anticipated raising more livestock after electricity became available. The Iowa
study showed that 19 percent of the farm operators
interviewed indicated that they kept more livestock
than they could have kept without electricity.[16]

About 25 percent of the farm operators in Sevilla and Caicedonia anticipated farming more land
after electricity became available. Only 4 percent
of the operators in the Iowa study indicated that
they farmed more land than would have been possible
without electrical equipment. This was a secondary
benefit from chore labor, eliminating labor peaks
and permitting the operators more time in the
fields during rush periods.[17]

In addition to increasing production, rural
electrification can make it possible to produce
better quality products. As a country's economy
develops, the need for improvement and uniformity
in the quality of perishable agricultural products
become increasingly important. For example, consumers become more particular in their purchases of
food items. Requirements as to sanitation and
quality of fluid milk become higher.

Rural electrification has an especially important role to play on dairy farms in areas such
as Colombia, Costa Rica, Nicaragua and Ecuador where
the climate is warm the year round. Production of
high-quality milk requires rapid cooling. Bacteria
count of milk increases at a geometric rate if milk
is not cooled to 40 to 50 degrees immediately after
milking.[18]

Electricity can be used in other ways to improve the quality of agricultural products in the
warm areas. Electric egg coolers are effective in

improving the market quality of eggs. Electric
freezing units can maintain the quality of meats
for a substantially longer period of time than
methods that are now being used.

One respondent in Caicedonia was using con-
trolled lighting in the poultry house to increase
egg production. Power for the lighting was being
produced with a small diesel generator plant. Con-
trolled lighting can also be used to shift peak egg
production to months when prices are higher.

Dependability also was a major anticipation
of the benefits to be derived from rural electrification for some of the operators in the project
areas. Reduction of losses in farm production
means a greater amount of production will be available to be marketed.

Electrical equipment can increase the dependability of farm operations by (1) improving the
timeliness of operations by reducing the serious-
ness of machinery breakdowns, reducing labor requirements and lengthening the effective workday
through the use of lights, (2) reducing fire hazards, and (3) obtaining more dependable temperature
controls for such operations as brooding and heating pigs and chicks, cooling milk and washing dairy
utensils.[19] In the Sevilla-Caicedonia and Palermo
areas electricity could provide the means for a dependable temperature control for drying coffee and
for producing panela.

Mechanization of agriculture makes farmers dependent upon machines especially during critical
production seasons. These machines require maintenance and repair. Facilities for quick repair
must be available in town or the farmer must have
his own shop equipment and knowledge to do his own
repair work. One respondent in Caicedonia was
planning to build his own shop as soon as electricity became available. He also was expecting to do
repair work for his neighbors.

Electricity and electrical equipment can facilitate the timeliness of operations by enabling
farm operators to work longer hours during peak
seasons.   This is particularly useful to dairy
farmers.   In the Sevilla-Caicedonia and Palermo
areas longer working hours will be useful in producing panela and during coffee harvesting time.
Some operators may do their repair work on machinery at night.

The lower risk of fire resulting from the use
of electrical equipment, compared with alternative
types of energy, can have an important effect on
production.   Oil heaters for brooding chicks is
considered hazardous and one operator said he would
increase his poultry operations when he could replace the oil heaters with electric lamps.

Security is an important aspect of production
in Sevilla and Caicedonia.   Electricity for security was one of the most anticipated benefits to be
derived from the rural electric cooperative.
Losses of farm products through acts of violence
means a reduction in farm production.   Thus, if rural electrification can provide the necessary security to eliminate this violence it can make a
substantial contribution to an increase in the
amount of products available for the market.

Still another contribution that rural electrification can make in the general area of technical
progress is in rural industrialization.   W. W.
Rostow has stated that the most important task in
most developing nations is to learn how to widen
the domestic market for the goods they produce
themselves.   In some of the developing areas "it
would be helpful to encourage the manufacture and
marketing in rural areas on a more effective basis
of both cheap agricultural equipment and the kinds
of consumer goods likely to constitute, at rural
levels of income, an incentive to accept and to
apply modern methods of agricultural productivity."[20]

It was apparent from the survey that electricity would contribute significantly to this aspect of development. In the rural areas respondents indicated they had plans for increasing production of brown sugar and for starting plants to produce starch. In the town of Sevilla it is expected that a reliable source of electric power will contribute substantially to the development of new industries and the expansion of old ones. A reliable source of electricity already has brought about some industrialization in Santo Domingo, Ecuador.

CAPITAL ACCUMULATION

New and improved methods of production tend to require large amounts of capital. But capital is not a natural resource. It results from the application of human labor to natural resources. Once the process is begun it is assisted by existing capital. However, capital is not a simple product of human labor, natural resources and existing capital.[21]

From the physical point of view, capital formation requires that a part of the productive resources of society be devoted to the production of new means of production rather than to the production of commodities and services for present consumption. From the economic point of view, the production of capital goods can go on only if people save or abstain from consuming a part of their money incomes.

If people were entirely willing to save, then saving would not be a factor of primary concern in economic growth. But because they are not, there is a problem of securing an amount of saving and capital formation adequate to meet the needs of economic growth.

> If the people of a country can produce surplus goods over and above present needs for consumption and if they have

> money incomes which more than suf-
> fice for their immediate consumption
> requirements, saving and capital pro-
> duction can take place, a greater
> surplus is produced, more capital
> goods can be turned out, and so on
> and on. Capital tends to grow like
> a snowball rolling down a hill.[22]

If the people spend all of their money incomes
on consumable goods, the prospects for saving and
capital formation are poor. This is the situation
that exists in most of the less developed countries.
In some cases where there is a rapid increase in
population, the surplus income above present consumption needs is absorbed by the increased population rather than going into saving and production
of capital goods.

Savings must be invested if there is to be
capital formation. In some cases saving and investment are conducted by the same people. For
example, a farmer in Sevilla may save because he
wants to invest in a coffee drier or a jeep to
transport the coffee to the market. Or perhaps he
wants to buy equipment to manufacture starch from
the yuca that he produces. The motives for saving
are many and varied. Often the funds saved are not
closely related to the investment opportunities
that exist.

In order to increase saving and investment in
the project areas the population must be willing
to reduce present consumption or be able to increase money income. Since consumption in the
areas already is at a relatively low level, it is
unlikely that the people will reduce significantly
their expenditures on consumable goods. In addition, it is contrary to human nature for an individual to reduce his present level of living for an
extended period. Therefore, it appears that the
best prospect for increasing saving and investment
in the project areas is through an increase in
income.

Farm income can be increased by reducing production costs while maintaining the same level of
production or by increasing the value of output by
a greater proportion than the value of input.

The survey in Sevilla showed that 50 percent
of the farms in the sample would reduce production
costs with the use of electricity. This savings
was brought about through the substitution of electric energy for fuels. The net result for the 50
farms in Sevilla, however, was that electricity
would increase farm energy costs 2 percent. This
was due primarily to increased uses of energy to
implement production plans. For the entire sample,
it was projected that energy costs with the availability of electricity would be reduced 50 percent.

If an increased energy cost did not reduce
farm income, then the value of production would
have to rise. If the value of production were to
increase by a greater amount than the value of inputs, including energy costs, then rural electrification would make a contribution to increasing
money income.

The survey in Sevilla showed that income would
increase on 85 percent of the farms. On the other
16 percent of the farms, income would decrease primarily because of additional energy costs. Net income for all farms, however, would increase approximately 10 percent. In terms of dollars using an
exchange rate of 13.5 pesos to 1 dollar this would
be an average annual increase in farm profit of
$757.

While the official exchange rate was Col $13.50
per $1.00, the free market exchange rate was rough-
ly 17.50 to 1 at the time final observations were
made. Using an exchange rate of 17.5 to 1 would
indicate an annual average increase per farm of
$584.

On the five farms studied by the South Western
Electricity Board in England, there was an annual

increase in profit per farm of $622.   This is
roughly the median of the results for using the official and free market exchange rates in Colombia.

One source of capital savings for some farms
will be the substitution of electric lighting for
conventional methods of lighting. At the lower
levels of farm income, lighting costs make up a
greater proportion of total farm expenditures. Demand for electricity on the lower income farms will
be almost exclusively for lighting.

In a study of cost analysis of electricity supply systems for rural communities, Ralph Hofmeister
states that "for evaluating the feasibility of domestic electric service, the key cost comparison is
between electric lighting and lamps or lanterns
fueled by kerosene--and also by gasoline, especially
in South America, as gasoline is a more satisfactory fuel for the high pressure mantle type of lan-
tern."[23]

Power expenditures for private generating
plants were by far the highest lighting costs in
the sample of farms. Candles were the next highest
with gas lamps third.

Hofmeister estimated a representative Indian
rural household now spending about $4.00 per year
for kerosene could obtain an equivalent level of
illumination with one 15-watt incandescent bulb at
a cost of $.83 per year.

> Even with a higher level of illumina-
> tion, annual capacity and energy costs
> for electricity are lower. A 25-watt
> bulb on the same basis implies annual
> costs of $1.40 and a 40-watt bulb,
> $2.00. In South America, both the
> market and the real social cost of
> kerosene and gasoline is much lower
> than in India. Hence the relative
> savings per unit of illumination are
> less than in India. However, due to

lower fuel prices and somewhat higher
incomes, the average level of use is
higher in South America.[24]

On 28 farms in Sevilla and Caicedonia the average annual cost for candle lighting was Col $125,
or $9.18 at an exchange rate of 13.5 to 1. Light-
ing with gas lamps on 22 farms averaged Col $123 or
$9.11. Since the minimum annual electric bill was
to be Col $60 or $4.44, the savings in lighting
costs could be approximately half of the cost of
lighting with fuel. At a retail rate of Col $.19
per kilowatt-hour, a 25-watt incandescent bulb
could be burned continuously and still not entirely
use the number of kilowatt-hours permitted by the
minimum bill. Thus, electricity would provide considerably better lighting than fuels and at the
same time the costs would be less.

In comparing electrification and petroleum
fuels for lighting, Hofmeister states that "personal incomes are higher in South America than in
India, and it is not implausible that many rural
extensions could be defended on the basis of domestic service exclusively."[25]

Rural electrification can also increase farm
income and hence contribute to capital accumulation
by making horizontal and vertical diversification
possible. Approximately half of the farmers in
Sevilla and Caicedonia were planning horizontal diversification. This is the growing of a wider
range of products to protect against loss of income
in case one crop fails or the price of one crop
drops substantially.

Some farmers indicated they would practice
vertical diversification. This is the carrying of
any one farm product through a processing stage to
make its marketing value higher and consequently
raise farm income. In Sevilla and Caicedonia vertical diversification would be carried out with the
help of electricity by such practices as cooling
milk, making starch from yuca, producing panela

from sugar cane, poultry and dairy processing and butchering beef and swine at the farms where the products are grown.

> Such diversification may best be applied, . . . where the holdings are small and the existing labor is not fully utilized or has time available now that electric power is available for facilitating the normal farm processes. Full consideration should be given to this aspect of economic returns to a projected rural supply scheme.[26]

INSTITUTIONAL DEVELOPMENT

A cooperative organization is "an economic institution through which economic activity is conducted in the pursuit of economic objectives."[27] Thus, a rural electric cooperative is an economic institution. Purchasing or generating and distributing electric energy is its primary economic activity. Supplying its members with electric service at the least cost possible is its primary economic objective.

Objectives of a cooperative and an independent electric firm are somewhat different. The most important economic objective of an independent firm is its striving for profit maximization. The purpose of a cooperative is the advancement of the interests of its members.[28]

In the case of a rural electric cooperative, the advancement of the interests of its members involves providing sufficient and reliable electric service at the least cost consistent with good business practices. The independent electric firm is concerned with the advancement of the interests of its stockholders. Operations of the independent firm, therefore, are aimed at profit maximization.

Profit maximization implies a financial return greater than the investment. In the rural areas of the less developed countries profit from rural electrification would necessarily be small or non-existent. Entrepreneurs, therefore, are not interested in investing in rural electrification.

Even if private investment capital were available and profits from rural electrification were attainable, the independent firm would not contribute to community development to the extent of a cooperative organization. Excess capital generated through operations of the independent firm would be returned to the investors. Usually, this would mean a fleeing of capital to the larger cities and away from the area where it is most needed. Higher retail rates, necessary to generate a competitive return on the investment, would also retard use of electricity in the distribution area.

Given the advantages of a cooperative organization over an independent firm for distribution of electricity in the rural areas of a less developed country, the question then arises as to government participation. It may be asked why the government should not go ahead and provide rural electrification rather than subsidizing a cooperative organization.

Several problems arise when a national or state government becomes involved in distribution of electricity in rural areas. In most cases the government does not have the manpower or capabilities for providing electric service for the entire country. For historical reasons, people of many of the less developed countries lack confidence in their governments. Their attitude toward officials of national, state and local government is generally that of mistrust.

In a small town in Costa Rica the government's power authority had to raise retail rates in order to comply with conditions of an international loan. The local population, not fully understanding the situation and lacking confidence in their government,

demonstrated violently against the increased rate.
Some demonstrators were killed and the townspeople
then refused to pay their electric bills. Because
of the volatile situation the government was afraid
to stop electric service; consequently, the town
and its population received free electric service
for more than a year.

Distribution of electricity is a monopolistic
situation. Monopoly "involves the risk that the
economic benefits of added efficiency will be diverted entirely to its owners. In such circum-
stances, cooperative organization is often the institutional arrangement most conducive to economic
welfare."[29]

The cooperative approach to development also
is recommended by Lauchlin Currie in a report to
the World Bank. Currie stated, "The growth of the
cooperative movement offers the hope of lessening
the burden that weighs on the public offices. We
recommend that this movement be promoted through
technical assistance, credit and other kinds of
help."[30]

NOTES

1. Ernesto Velez and Ernest Feder, The Lagging Growth of the Cooperative Movement in Colombia
(Bogota: Ministerio de Agricultura, August, 1961),
p. 16.

2. Richard Rutter, "Education in U.S. Big and
Growing," The New York Times, September 5, 1965,
p. 10.

3. George Ivan Smith, "The 'Human Factor' in
Economic Development," International Development
Review, V, no. 2 (June, 1963), 14.

4. Paavo Kaarlehto, "On the Economic Nature
of Cooperation," Acta Agriculturae Scandinavica
(Stockholm), VI, no. 3 (1956), 282.

5. R. C. Woodworth and R. R. Beneke, Electricity in Farm Production, Agriculture Information Bulletin No. 100 (Washington: U.S. Department of Agriculture, May, 1953), p. 6.

6. Ibid.

7. Ibid., p. 9.

8. W. J. Buscott, "The Economics of Farming by Electricity," Journal I.E.E., November, 1956, p. 652.

9. V. Baker, Electricity and the Farm Business, Selected Papers in Agricultural Economics, Vol. VII, No. 2, Department of Economics, University of Bristol (Bristol: n.d.), p. 71.

10. Woodworth and Beneke, op. cit., p. 9.

11. James Reston, "New Delhi: The Real War on Poverty," The New York Times, December 15, 1965, p. 46.

12. Fernando Torrent (Acting Executive Director, Puerto Rico Water Resources Authority, San Juan, Puerto Rico), personal letter received October 7, 1965. Refers to Analisis de Algunos Cambios Recientes en la Poblacion de Puerto Rico (San Juan: Universidad de Puerto Rico, September, 1964).

13. Gerald M. Meier and Robert E. Baldwin, Economic Development-Theory: History, Policy (New York: John Wiley & Son, 1957), p. 279.

14. W. I. Myers, "The Role of Education in Agricultural Development," in Roger Dixey, ed., International Explorations of Agricultural Economics (Ames: University of Iowa Press, 1964), p. 178.

15. E. W. Golding, "Stepping Up Output From the Land," Electric Power, I, no. 3 (April, 1963), 42.

16. Woodworth and Beneke, op. cit., p. 13.

17. Ibid.

18. Ibid., p. 14.

19. Ibid., p. 12.

20. W. W. Rostow, "Agriculture's Role in Economic Development," Foreign Agriculture, Vol. I (September 2, 1963), p. 5.

21. R. H. Blodgett, Our Expanding Economy (New York: Rinehart & Company, 1955), p. 48.

22. Ibid., p. 90.

23. Ralph H. Hofmeister, Cost Analysis of Electricity Supply Systems for Rural Communities (Cambridge, Mass.: Center for International Studies, Massachusetts Institute of Technology, under General Electric Subcontract, March, 1963), p. 153.

24. Ibid., p. 158.

25. Ibid., p. 159.

26. United Nations, Economic and Social Council, Rural Electrification, Reports Prepared by the Experts, Vol. II (Geneva: U.N., March, 1954), p. 6.

27. Richard Philipps, "Economic Nature of the Cooperative Association," Journal of Farm Economics, XXXV, no. 1 (February, 1953), 74.

28. Leslie E. Drayton, "Cooperatives and Economic Welfare," Journal of Farm Economics, XXXIV, no. 4 (November, 1952), 557.

29. Smith, loc. cit.

30. Lauchlin Currie, Bases de un Programa de Fomento para Colombia, Mision Economica para Colombia, auspiciado por el Banco de Reconstruccion y Fomento, Banco de la Republica, Bogota, Colombia, 1951.

7

CONCLUSION:
POLICY
IMPLICATIONS

The theoretical framework for the study was based on three prerequisites for development--minimum levels of effective government, education and motivation. Given these prerequisites, the main factors limiting the rate of development according to the model were population growth, capital accumulation, technical progress and institutional structure.

SUMMARY OF FINDINGS

Indications are that the cooperative organization will play its greatest role in improving the preconditions for development and the institutional structure, while rural electrification will have its greatest effect on the factors limiting development.

Operation of the rural electric cooperatives will be in close association with state and national governments. Personnel of the government agencies will have an opportunity to work closely with rural people. This close working relationship will permit government administrators to become better

acquainted with the problems of rural development.
A successful working partnership between government
and the rural population will help build confidence
in government.

Improved knowledge of the existing rural situation and an understanding of agricultural problems
will assist government officials in doing a better
job of public administration. As the organ of public administration becomes more competent, technical knowledge and capital investment will pay
greater dividends. Organization of the rural electric cooperative in Sevilla, Colombia, caused a political awakening of the rural community. Leaders
of the rural electric cooperative in Santo Domingo,
Ecuador, worked to raise the political and administrative level of the area to be served by the cooperative. And in one area cooperative members vot-
ing at their first meeting said they felt that this
was the first time their vote would be counted.

Cooperative rural electrification should have
a significant effect on education in the pilot
project areas. Electric lighting has improved
study room conditions and provides an opportunity
for adult education at night. Electrification has
improved living conditions for teachers residing at
the schools. Most of the schools now have electric
lights. Teachers indicated the schools would purchase radios, irons, fans, refrigerators, water
pumps and in some cases television sets and electric stoves. Some teachers also expressed the hope
that school lunch programs would be started as a
result of electrification.

Economic development planning must not overlook the human resources. It must take into consideration qualities of the community and the desire of the people to develop. The spirit of cooperation can be a valuable contribution to motivation for development. Members of the pilot rural
electric cooperatives provided right-of-way easements without cost, they donated land to construct
office and generating facilities, they cleared land

without cost for construction of distribution lines and they volunteered their time and labor to build the systems.   All of these contributions reduced costs making the projects feasible.   In Santo Domingo, Ecuador, a large percentage of the cooperative members make monthly payments voluntarily at the office before being presented their bills.

It was apparent from the field studies that rural electrification would have a greater beneficial effect on farms that already were consuming substantial amounts of energy.   Rural electrification was expected to increase income on 84 percent of the farms surveyed.   Increased income was anticipated to result in some cases from higher production and in other cases from lower energy costs.

Results of the survey did not indicate that rural electrification would have much effect on incomes of small farms that were not farmed intensively.   In most cases, however, costs for electricity would be covered by increased production or by savings through the substitution of electricity for fuels.   Therefore, their level of living would be improved considerably through the use of electric lights and appliances at little or no cost to the economy.

Survey results also indicated that rural electrification would contribute to diversification of agriculture, thus benefiting not only the individual farmer but also the economy of the country. Where each farm was producing 1.75 product for the market, it was expected to produce 2.33 product with electricity.   This 33 percent increase in diversification, if realized, should have a favorable effect on income.

In many areas of the less developed countries, security is an important aspect of production.   Security was one of the three benefits most anticipated by potential rural electric consumers.   The first two benefits were saving time and reducing costs.   Prevention of loss of production caused by

banditry and violence serves to increase the amount
available for market. Thus, security can increase
farm income.

In addition to increasing agricultural production, rural electrification can make it possible to
produce better quality products. As a country's
economy develops, the need for improvement and uniformity in the quality of perishable agricultural
products becomes increasingly important.

Rural electrification has an especially important role to play in countries with warm climates.
Food processing and refrigeration of meat, dairy
and poultry products will prevent loss and improve
quality. By preventing food loss, more food becomes available for consumption and the end result
is the same as that of increasing production.

Other technical benefits of rural electrification include increasing the dependability of farm
operations, reducing fire hazards, obtaining more
dependable temperature control, facilitating the
timeliness of farm operations and providing opportunities for cottage crafts and rural industrialization.

There were no indications that electricity
would replace farm labor. On the contrary approximately one third of the farmers indicated they
would hire more labor after electricity became
available. Thus, rural electrification gives prom-
ise of reducing migration from the agricultural
areas to the overcrowded urban centers.

Migration from the rural areas for the conveniences of city life, along with a rapidly expanding population, has plagued development. The rapidly increasing population in the developing countries is the one factor most limiting economic
development. Total population of these countries
doubles about every quarter century. With a population growth of 3 percent, agricultural production
must increase the same amount simply to feed and

clothe the increased population. Add to this the
demand for improved nutrition and increased agricultural exports, and the role of agriculture becomes critical.

While there are no studies on the effect of
rural electrification on population growth, there
are some noteworthy observations. India's Food
Minister has pointed out that in Madras, 80 percent
of the rural villages have electricity and the
birth rate is about half as large as the national
birth rate. In Puerto Rico there was a declining
birth rate in the rural areas during the 1950-60
decade. This was precisely the period when Puerto
Rico launched its rural electrification program.
No research has been conducted to show a causal relationship but it has been pointed out that rural
electrification opened a means of communication
through which birth control information was given
to the public.

The institutional arrangement of distributing
electricity through a cooperative offers several
advantages. In Nicaragua members of the rural
electric cooperative formed a water cooperative and
constructed a well. In Colombia the cooperative
was instrumental in creating social justice and
eliminating political favors through the use of
meters for all electric consumers. In Ecuador the
pilot project provided the pattern for establishing
a second rural electric cooperative and in laying
the groundwork for a cooperative water system.

The cooperative mechanism offers a means for
getting electricity to rural areas that otherwise
would not be electrified for many years. It unites
a rural community with a common cause. The organization then provides a pattern for other development projects. It offers the hope of improved living conditions, such as the use of electric lights,
radios, irons, utility motors, refrigerators, television sets, water systems, washing machines, chick
incubators, sewing machines, stoves, security
alarms, deep freezes, blenders, etc. These were

the intended uses of electricity in their order of
importance according to the field survey of potential consumers.

POLICY IMPLICATIONS

Experience in the pilot rural electric cooperative areas indicates that a rural electrification
program will be more viable if rural towns, villages and farms are treated as a unit. Not only
will an electrification project be more feasible in
the rural area, but it will also permit a higher
rate of growth in the town because of development
in the surrounding agricultural area.

Treating rural towns, village and farms as an
economic unit will permit the costs of distribution
to be averaged out. Otherwise, rural consumers
would be required to pay a greater amount because
of the higher cost in extending distribution lines
to the farms. Few of the rural consumers would be
in a financial position to pay the greater amount
and quite probably they would go without central
station service. A program requiring rural consumers to pay more than town consumers would not
only stifle growth in the rural areas but it would
also retard growth in the towns. In addition, it
would tend to create friction between the rural
population and the town population.

An "averaging out" rural electrification program will permit a maximum number of consumers to
be served with the available distribution lines.
Such a program should also include the "area cover-
age" concept. That is, all persons in the area of
the electric cooperative should be given an opportunity to become a member and receive electric
service.

Experience in the pilot project areas also indicates that it is not necessarily the best policy
to begin a rural electrification program in the
most economically feasible area. In Sevilla and

Caicedonia social and political considerations were of prime importance. Other areas in the Department of Valle appeared to be more economically feasible for a rural electrification program, but because of the violence and social unrest the need for development was greatest in the Municipios of Sevilla and Caicedonia.

Remembering that political and social stability are prerequisites to development, it may be more advantageous to overall development of the country to begin a rural electrification program in an area that is not the most economically feasible. That is, the political and social needs may outweigh the desired economic changes.

In view of the limitation on funds, implications are that a cooperative rural electrification program should be undertaken first in the particular area of a developing country that has the greatest development needs taking into consideration all economic, social and political factors.

CONCLUSION

Several factors complicate a projection of returns from using electricity in rural areas. Benefits cannot be considered entirely from the standpoint of immediate monetary returns. Returns may be secondary in nature, that is, they may depend upon the use of time and labor saved. Furthermore, it is difficult to separate the contribution of electrical equipment from other factors that may change.

Benefits of electricity have been evaluated primarily in terms of individual enterprises. Overall benefits, however, are more than a summation of benefits on individual enterprises. Overall benefits may include a multiplier effect on the local economy as the result of a specific investment in electrification. In addition, cooperative rural electrification may provide indirect benefits that are difficult to quantify.

Notwithstanding the positive implications of cooperative rural electrification for economic and social development, it is evident that electrification by itself is not the answer to overall development. Many more types of development activities in the project areas are needed, such as education, technical training, credit, roads, marketing facilities and institutional organization.

The rural electric cooperative can help in providing the pattern for carrying out these other development activities. As members of the community are exposed to the conveniences of electricity and a better way of life, their motivation to work on other community development projects will increase.

Perhaps the greatest contribution of cooperative rural electrification in developing countries will be that of a prime mover in development--as a catalyst to the desire to develop.

BIBLIOGRAPHY

Asociacion Nacional de Industriales. Cali and the
    Cauca Valley. Cali: ANDI, 1964.

Baker, V. Electricity and the Farm Business.
    Selected papers in Agricultural Economics,
    Vol. VII, No. 2, Department of Economics, Uni-
    versity of Bristol. Bristol: n.d.

Banco de la Republica. A Guide for the Investor.
    Bogota: n.d.

Burr, Mildred. "Basic Data on the Economy of Ecua-
    dor." Washington: U.S. Department of Com-
    merce.

Buscott, W. J. "The Economics of Farming by Elec-
    tricity," Journal I.E.E., November, 1956.

Butler, William F. "Differential Rates of Growth,
    Developed and Underdeveloped Nations and Their
    Implications," Journal of Farm Economics, XLVI,
    no. 5 (December, 1964).

Childs, John F. Long-Term Financing. Englewood
    Cliffs, N.J.: Prentice-Hall, Inc., 1961.

Cooperativa de Caficultores de Caicedonia Ltd.
    "Information Socio-Economica del Municipio de
    Caicedonia," Valle, Colombia. Unpublished re-
    port, 1963.

Corporacion Autonoma Regional del Cauca. El Sector
    Agropecuario. Cali: CVC, Division de Planea-
    cion Regional, September, 1965.

_____. Loan Application for the Se-Ca Rural Elec-
    tric Cooperative. Cali: CVC, 1963.

Currie, Lauchlin. Bases de un Programa de Fomento
    para Colombia, Mision Economica para Colombia,
    auspiciado por el Banco de Reconstruccion y
    Fomento, Banco de la Republica, Bogota, Colom-
    bia, 1951.

Drayton, Leslie E.   "Cooperatives and Economic Wel-
    fare," Journal of Farm Economics, XXXIV, no. 4
    (November, 1952).

Fajardo Chaves, Jorge Enrique (Comandante del
    Batallon, Octava Brigada, Ejercito Nacional
    Republica de Colombia).   Letter dated March
    12, 1965.

Forrest, Leo.   "Pilot Rural Electrification Projects,
    Norte de Santander, Colombia." Mimeographed.
    Washington: National Rural Electric Coopera-
    tive Association, April 5, 1963.

Galbraith, John K.   Economic Development in Per-
    spective. Cambridge, Mass.:   Harvard Univer-
    sity Press, 1962.

Gislason, Conrad.   "Cooperatives and Resource Allo-
    cation," Journal of Farm Economics, XXXIV,
    no. 4 (November, 1952).

Golding, E. W.   "Stepping Up Output from the Land,"
    Electric Power, I, no. 3 (April, 1963).

_____ and Stodhart, A. H.   The Potentials for Rural
    Electrification in Asia and the Far East, In-
    formal Working Bulletin 22.   Rome: Food and
    Agriculture Organization.

Guscott, W. J.   "The Economics of Farming by Elec-
    tricity," Journal I.E.E., November, 1956.

Heady, Earl O.   Economics of Agricultural Produc-
    tion and Resource Use. Englewood Cliffs, N.J.:
    Prentice-Hall, 1952.

_____ and Tweeten, Luther G.   Resource Demand and
    Structure of the Agricultural Industry. Ames:
    Iowa State University Press, 1963.

Hofmeister, Ralph H.   Cost Analysis of Electricity
    Supply Systems for Rural Communities. Cam-
    bridge, Mass.:   Center for International Stud-
    ies, Massachusetts Institute of Technology,
    under General Electric Subcontract, March, 1963.

Kaarlehto, Paavo. "Cooperation as a Form of Eco-
    nomic Integration," _Acta Agriculturae Scandi-
    navica_ (Stockholm), V, no. 1 (1954-55).

_____. "On the Economic Nature of Cooperation,"
    Acta Agriculturae Scandinavica (Stockholm),
    VI, no. 3 (1956).

Lindstrom, David D. "Influence of Rural Institu-
    tions on Economic Development." Paper pre-
    sented at the University of Illinois, Depart-
    ment of Agricultural Economics Conference on
    Agriculture in Economic Development: Identi-
    fying Research Tasks for Agricultural Econo-
    mists, April 13, 14 and 15, 1964.

Moncada, Alonso. _Un Aspecto de la Violencia_.
    Bogota: 1963.

Montenegro Cabrera, Capitan Cesar (Secretario,
    Benemerito Cuerpo de Bomberos Voluntarios,
    Sevilla, Colombia). Letter report, March,
    1965.

Moses, Galen C. "Cooperative Rural Electrification
    in Costa Rica." Unpublished Masters thesis,
    University of Florida, 1969.

Mosher, A. T. "The Sociologist in Agricultural De-
    velopment," _Rural Sociology_, XXIX, no. 1.

Murray, William. "Preliminary Report on Distribu-
    tors of Energy." Unpublished typewritten re-
    port submitted to the Executive Director of
    CVC, Cali, Colombia, October 7, 1965.

Myers, W. I. "The Role of Education in Agricul-
    tural Development," in Roger Dixey, ed., _Inter-
    national Explorations of Agricultural Economics_.
    Ames: University of Iowa Press, 1964.

Pardo H., Diego. "Rural Electrification Program--
    Department of Valle," Corporacion Autonoma
    Regional del Cauca. Letter dated October 13,
    1965.

Phillips, Richard. "Economic Nature of the Cooperative Association," Journal of Farm Economics, XXXV, no. 1 (February, 1953).

Reston, James. "New Delhi: The Real War on Poverty," The New York Times, December 15, 1965.

Rostow, W. W. "Agriculture's Role in Economic Development," Foreign Agriculture, Vol. 11 (September 2, 1963).

Rutter, Richard. "Education in U.S. Big and Growing," The New York Times, September 5, 1965.

Sahlman, Frank M. and Fayette, Frederick J. Economic and Social Development Through Rural Electric Cooperatives. East Montpelier, Vermont: Washington Electric Cooperative, December 8, 1961.

Servicio Nacional de Aprendizaje. Estudio Socio-Economico del Area del Valle del Cauca. Bogota: SENA, Seccion de Investigaciones, 1962.

Smith, George Ivan. "The 'Human Factor' in Economic Development," International Development Review, V, no. 2 (June, 1963).

Stewart, Andrew. Rural Electrification in Alberta-- A Report to the Research Council of Alberta. Edmonton, Alberta, Canada, March, 1944.

Strong, Louis B. Investigation and Organization of Two Pilot Demonstration Electric Cooperatives. Washington: National Rural Electric Cooperative Association, 1963.

Subcommittee on Evaluation Standards, Report to the Inter-Agency Committee on Water Resources. Proposed Practices for Economic Analysis of River Basin Projects. Washington: May, 1958.

Survey Team from the U.S. Department of Agriculture,
    U.S. Department of Interior and Land Grant Uni-
    versities, Rural Development in Colombia--
    Evaluation and Recommendations. Washington:
    Department of State, Rural Development Series
    No. 4, October-November, 1963.

Torrent, Fernando (Acting Executive Director, Puerto
    Rico Water Resources Authority, San Juan,
    Puerto Rico). Letter received October 7, 1965.
    Refers to Analisis de Algunos Cambios Recientes
    en la Poblacion de Puerto Rico. San Juan:
    Universidad de Puerto Rico, September, 1964.

United Nations, Economic and Social Council. Rural
    Electrification. Reports prepared by the Ex-
    perts, Vol. II. Geneva: U.N., March, 1954.

U.S., Department of Agriculture, Association of
    State Universities and Land-Grant Colleges and
    Agency for International Development. "Report
    of Rural Development Team on Agriculture and
    Rural Development in Nicaragua," March-April,
    1964.

U.S., Department of Agriculture Survey Team. "Re-
    port and Recommendation of the U.S.D.A. Survey
    Team to USAID/Ecuador," November, 1963.

Universidad del Valle. Censo Agropecuario del Valle
    del Cauca, 1959. Cali: Facultad de Ciencias
    Economicas, 1963.

Velez, Ernesto and Feder, Ernest. The Lagging
    Growth of the Cooperative Movement in Colombia.
    Bogota: Ministerio de Agricultura, August,
    1961.

Woodworth, R. C. and Beneke, R. R. Electricity in
    Farm Production. Agriculture Information
    Bulletin No. 100. Washington: U.S. Depart-
    ment of Agriculture, May, 1953.

DR. JAMES E. ROSS, Assistant Director of International Programs in Agriculture at the Univeristy of Florida, has devoted his graduate education and professional career to international agricultural trade and development. His interest in international development combined with practical experience in cooperative rural electrification prompted the studies on which this book is based.

From 1959-61 Dr. Ross served as an international agricultural economist with the U.S. Department of Agriculture's Foreign Agricultural Service. He then joined the National Rural Electric Cooperative Association as a staff economist. In 1962 he became coordinator of the Association's first technical assistance contract with the U.S. Agency for International Development.

His foreign experience includes two and a half years as agricultural advisor to Costa Rica's National Planning Office and Export-Investment Promotion Center; one year with Ghana's Ministry of Economic Affairs conducting studies on marketing and processing of agricultural products; and travels through most Latin American countries, West and North Africa, Europe, Scandinavia and Southeast Asia.

Dr. Ross holds two B.S. degrees, one in general agriculture and one in journalism. He has M.S. and Ph.D. degrees from the Iniversity of Illinois in agricultural economics. He also has studied agricultural and international economics at the University of Maryland and the American University in Washington, D.C.

WAGNU